History Alive!®
The United States Through Industrialism

Chief Executive Officer: Bert Bower

Chief Operating Officer: Amy Larson

Director of Curriculum: Liz Russell

Managing Editor: Laura Alavosus

Editorial Project Manager: Nancy Rogier

Project Editor: Mali Apple

Copyeditor: Jennifer Seidel

Editorial Associates: Anna Embree, Sarah Sudano

Production Manager: Lynn Sanchez

Art Director: John F. Kelly

Senior Graphic Designers: Christy Uyeno, Paul Rebello

Graphic Designers: Don Taka, Victoria Philp

Photo Edit Manager: Margee Robinson

Photo Editor: Picture Research Consultants, Inc.

Production Project Manager: Eric Houts

Art Editor: Mary Swab

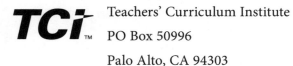

Teachers' Curriculum Institute

PO Box 50996

Palo Alto, CA 94303

Customer Service: 800-497-6138

www.teachtci.com

ISBN 978-1-58371-935-0

2 3 4 5 6 7 8 9 10 -MLI- 15 14 13 12

Manufactured by Malloy Lithographers, Ann Arbor, MI
United States of America, Jan. 2012, Job #259120

Program Director

Bert Bower

Program Author

Diane Hart

Creative Development Manager

Kelly Shafsky

Contributing Writers

Laura Alavosus

John Bergez

Susan Buckley

Jill Fox

Christine Freeman

Amy George

Brent Goff

Andrew Goldblatt

David M. Holford

Elspeth Leacock

Tedd Levy

Julie Weiss

Curriculum Developers

Joyce Bartky

April Bennett

Nicole Boylan

Vern Cleary

Terry Coburn

Julie Cremin

Erin Fry

Amy George

Steve Seely

Nathan Wellborne

Reading Specialist

Kate Kinsella, Ed.D.
*Reading and TESOL Specialist
San Francisco State University*

Teacher Consultants

Melissa Aubuchon
*City of Ladue School District
St. Louis, Missouri*

Terry Coburn
*Brookside School
Stockton, California*

Connie Davidson
*San Leandro Unified School
District
San Leandro, California*

Amy George
*Weston Middle School
Weston, Massachusetts*

Nicolle Hutchinson
*Broward County Public Schools
Miramar, Florida*

Dawn Lavond
*Moreland Middle School
San Jose, California*

Julie Peters
*Woodstock Community Union
School District #200
Woodstock, Illinois*

Debra Schneider
*Tracy Unified School District
Tracy, California*

Acknowledgments

Scholars

Dr. Eric Avila
*University of California,
Los Angeles*

Maureen Booth
Maynard, Massachusetts

Dr. Eun Mi Cho
*California State University
Sacramento*

Dr. William Deverell
University of Southern California

Dr. Dan Dupre
*University of North Carolina,
Charlotte*

Dr. Ben Keppel
University of Oklahoma

Dr. Stanley J. Underdal
San Jose State University

Dr. Dan Wickburg
University of Texas, Dallas

Readability Consultant

Jeanne Barry
*Jeanne Barry and Associates, Inc.
Incline Village, Nevada*

Cartographer

Mapping Specialists
Madison, Wisconsin

Internet Consultant

Chuck Taft
*University School of Milwaukee
Milwaukee, Wisconsin*

Diverse Needs Consultants

Erin Fry
Glendora, California

Colleen Guccione
Naperville, Illinois

Cathy Hix
*Swanson Middle School
Arlington, Virginia*

Directions for Analyzing
American Indian Artifacts

In this activity, you will examine placards with drawings of artifacts from eight American Indian cultural regions. Follow these steps for each placard:

Step 1: With your partner, examine the artifacts shown. Using the four maps in Section 1.3 of your book, hypothesize which American Indian cultural region the artifacts came from. Write the placard letter in the corresponding column of the matrix in your Reading Notes.

Step 2: Check with your teacher to make sure you have identified the correct cultural region.

Step 3: In the column for that cultural region, fill in at least two pieces of information the artifacts reveal.

Step 4: Read the section in your book about that cultural region. Complete the Reading Notes for that section.

Step 5: Move to an open placard. Repeat Steps 1 to 4 until you have examined all the placards and completed your Reading Notes.

Chapter 1 Assessment

Mastering the Content

Fill in the circle next to the best answer.

1. How do scientists think people migrated from Asia to the Americas during the last Ice Age?
   ○ A. They sailed across a narrow strait.
   ○ B. They traveled south from Canada.
   ○ C. They traveled across a land bridge.
   ○ D. They sailed to Mexico and then drifted north.

2. Why did the first Americans migrate from Asia to the Americas?
   ○ A. in search of food
   ○ B. to locate fertile farmland
   ○ C. to flee from hostile tribes
   ○ D. in search of a better climate

3. Which of these characterizes an American Indian cultural region?
   ○ A. People migrated together.
   ○ B. People have the same leader.
   ○ C. People share a similar language.
   ○ D. People come from the same family.

4. Which of these best explains why different cultural regions formed in North America?
   ○ A. Groups settled in the areas at various times.
   ○ B. Groups chose where they lived based on their special skills.
   ○ C. Groups needed to distinguish themselves from other groups.
   ○ D. Groups adapted to the environments in which they settled.

5. Which of these describes how American Indians viewed their environment?
   ○ A. They believed they owned the land on which they lived.
   ○ B. They believed that the land should remain unchanged.
   ○ C. They believed they were a part of a community of living things.
   ○ D. They believed they were the rulers of the region in which they lived.

6. Which of these was most important to the survival of the American Indians?
   ○ A. land and home ownership
   ○ B. trade to meet their daily needs
   ○ C. ability to use natural resources
   ○ D warm and mild climate conditions

7. How do historians learn how American Indians lived so long ago?
   ○ A. They read their journals.
   ○ B. They study their artifacts.
   ○ C. They live in their shelters.
   ○ D. They speak to their families.

8. How did the American Indians in the Southeast live?
   ○ A. They lived in wooden longhouses in the forest.
   ○ B. They lived in adobe villages on top of flat mesas.
   ○ C. They lived in underground pit houses beside major rivers.
   ○ D. They lived in towns clustered around large earthen mounds.

9. American Indians who lived on the Plains wore clothing made from animal hides. Which of these was an important economic activity in this region?
   ○ A. fishing
   ○ B. mining
   ○ C. hunting
   ○ D. gathering

10. Which of these describes one way American Indians adapted the environment to meet their needs?
   ○ A. Northwest Coast people ate fish.
   ○ B. Southwest people made many things with corn.
   ○ C. Great Plains people made clothing from animal hides.
   ○ D. Eastern Woodlands people burned trees to plant corn.

11. Which of these enabled American Indians to settle in permanent villages?
   ○ A. trading
   ○ B. hunting
   ○ C. herding
   ○ D. farming

12. Which of these was an important resource of the Northwest Coast people?
   ○ A. Great Lakes
   ○ B. Pacific Ocean
   ○ C. Gulf of Mexico
   ○ D. Mississippi River

13. Which of these was most important in determining the way of life of an American Indian group?
   ○ A. food sources
   ○ B. language skills
   ○ C. land ownership
   ○ D. religious celebrations

14. Which of these was a strong influence on the kind of shelters used by each American Indian group?
   ○ A. wealth
   ○ B. climate
   ○ C. religion
   ○ D. education

15. Which conditions challenged the survival of American Indians in the Southwest?
   ○ A. extreme cold and flat land
   ○ B. dense forests and wild animals
   ○ C. high temperatures and lack of water
   ○ D. dangerous storms and flooded fields

16. How was it possible for the mesa people to grow corn in the desert?
   ○ A. They used rain barrels.
   ○ B. They dug irrigation ditches.
   ○ C. They traded their crops for water.
   ○ D. They planted drought-tolerant corn.

Applying Social Studies Skills

Use the map and your knowledge of history to answer the questions.

American Indian Cultural Regions

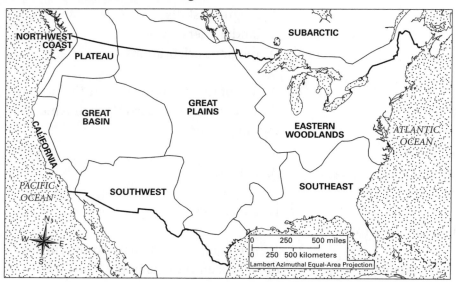

17. Read the list.

   > dense grasses
   > treeless grasslands
   > large buffalo herds

   Which cultural region is described by this information?

18. What was one important resource for American Indians of the Eastern Woodlands?

19. The American Indians were resourceful people. Which cultural region do you think required the most resourcefulness? Briefly explain why you think so, and support your reasoning with facts.

Exploring the Essential Question

How did the first Americans adapt to their environments?

Follow the directions to complete the item below.

20. Choose two of the following cultural regions—Northwest Coast, California, Plateau, Great Basin, Southeast, or Eastern Woodlands—and draw an artifact that was or may have been discovered in each of those regions. Write a paragraph about each of your two artifacts that

    • describes how it is made, including the materials used.

    • explains its uses.

    • explains how it shows adaptation to that cultural region.

    Make sure to convey your ideas clearly, using standard English.

Creating an Act-It-Out About Columbus Claiming San Salvador

Your group will bring to life one character in the image of Columbus claiming San Salvador for Spain. Your teacher will select one member of your group to play the part of your assigned character. A reporter will then interview the characters.

Step 1: Circle the character your group has been assigned.

Christopher Columbus

Priest

Soldier

Taino Indian

Step 2: Discuss the questions for your character. Make sure everyone in your group can answer your character's questions so that everyone is prepared to be the actor.

Columbus, Priest, and Soldier

Where are you from?

Why are you carrying swords?

Why have you brought a priest?

Where do you think you have landed?

What did you expect to find?

What do you think of the people you have found here?

Taino Indian

Who are you?

What do you find most unusual about these new people who have arrived?

Why do you think these men (Columbus and his crew) have come here?

Will you treat these men as friends or enemies? Why or why not?

Step 3: Discuss how the person who is chosen to perform can make the character come alive through facial expressions, tone of voice, and posture. Collect simple props to use during the act-it-out.

Creating an Act-It-Out About New France

Your group will bring to life one character in the image of coureurs de bois working in New France. Your teacher will select one member from your group to play the part of your assigned character. A reporter will then interview the characters.

Step 1: Circle the character your group has been assigned.

Coureur de Bois Holding Fish

Coureur de Bois Holding a Fox

Huron Indian

Iroquois Indian

Step 2: Discuss the questions for your character. Make sure everyone in your group can answer your character's questions so that everyone is prepared to be the actor.

Coureurs de Bois

Who are you?

What does coureurs de bois mean in English?

Why did you come to New France?

Why have so few French people settled here?

What type of relationship do you have with American Indians in the area?

Huron and Iroquois Indians

Who are you?

What enemies do you have in the area?

Have you supported or fought against the French settlers who live in this area? Why?

Has the arrival of the French in this area helped or hurt American Indians living in this region? How?

Step 3: Discuss how the person who is chosen to perform can make the character come alive through facial expressions, tone of voice, and posture. Collect simple props to use during the act-it-out.

Chapter 2 Assessment

Mastering the Content

Fill in the circle next to the best answer.

1. How did Marco Polo encourage European exploration?
   - ○ A. He became wealthy after conquering the Incas.
   - ○ B. He wrote a book about his travels in Asia.
   - ○ C. He told stories about his trip around the tip of Africa.
   - ○ D. He brought treasures back from his journey to the Americas.

2. Which of these was a major motivation for European exploration?
   - ○ A. profit
   - ○ B. leisure
   - ○ C. freedom
   - ○ D. education

3. Which of these was a goal of the first European explorers?
   - ○ A. to establish trading posts
   - ○ B. to find a water route to Asia
   - ○ C. to exchange ideas with native peoples
   - ○ D. to explore North and South America

4. How did the Columbian Exchange affect many American Indian groups?
   - ○ A. They grew in number.
   - ○ B. They died from diseases.
   - ○ C. They became prosperous.
   - ○ D. They were forced to move.

5. Which of these describes the relationship between the French and the American Indians?
   - ○ A. They were enemies.
   - ○ B. They were business partners.
   - ○ C. The French converted the American Indians.
   - ○ D. The American Indians were slaves to the French.

6. Which of these was a goal of the Spanish conquistadors who came to the Americas?
   - ○ A. to trade with the native peoples
   - ○ B. to conquer a large empire for Spain
   - ○ C. to establish agricultural communities
   - ○ D. to learn about the culture of the Aztec people

7. What was the main goal of the Spanish missionaries?
   - ○ A. to protect the American Indians
   - ○ B. to trade with the American Indians
   - ○ C. to teach their religion to the American Indians
   - ○ D. to learn about the customs of the American Indians

8. Which of these settled in the Spanish borderlands?
   - ○ A. farmers and ranchers
   - ○ B. soldiers and missionaries
   - ○ C. pirates and runaway slaves
   - ○ D. miners and treasure seekers

9. Which statement is true about slavery in North America?

○ A. American Indian slaves were treated with dignity.
○ B. European explorers rejected slavery in the Americas.
○ C. Slavery had not existed before the European discovery of America.
○ D. African slaves took the place of American Indian workers.

10. What was an important economic activity of both the French and Dutch settlements?

○ A. fur trade
○ B. slave trade
○ C. tobacco farming
○ D. sugar cane farming

11. Which of these describes the experience of the first Jamestown settlers?

○ A. They were challenged by the environment.
○ B. They found the area already settled by the Dutch.
○ C. They were welcomed by the American Indians.
○ D. They quickly established a prosperous settlement.

12. What was an effect of Christopher Columbus's voyages to the Americas?

○ A. a reduction in the European population
○ B. a delay in future Spanish explorations
○ C. a war between the Spanish and the French
○ D. a transfer of foods between Europe and the Americas

13. Why did the London Company send settlers to Virginia?

○ A. to create maps of the area
○ B. to establish a trading post
○ C. to start a moneymaking colony
○ D. to make peace with American Indians

14. What event helped end conflict between the Jamestown settlers and the American Indians?

○ A. the arrival of Captain John Smith
○ B. the marriage of John Rolfe to Pocahontas
○ C. the discovery of the lost colony of Roanoke
○ D. the success of the trade of weapons and food

15. In which way was New Amsterdam different from other European settlements?

○ A. It included only Dutch people.
○ B. It was led by an American Indian.
○ C. It included a diverse population.
○ D. It was founded on religious beliefs.

16. Which of these became the name of New Netherland after the English took it over in 1664?

○ A. New York
○ B. New Jersey
○ C. New England
○ D. New Hampshire

Applying Social Studies Skills

Use the drawing and your knowledge of history to answer the questions.

The drawing illustrates a battle between Samuel Champlain and his Huron allies and a group of Iroquois warriors. The passage is Champlain's description of the event.

> *I marched some 20 paces ahead of the rest, until I was about 30 paces from the enemy . . . When I saw them making a move to fire at us, I rested my musket against my cheek and aimed directly at one of their three chiefs. With the same shot, two fell to the ground, and one of their men was wounded . . . When our side saw this shot . . . they began to raise such loud cries that one could not have heard it thunder. Meanwhile, the arrows flew on both sides.*

17. According to the passage, what caused Samuel Champlain to fire his musket?

18. Which of these statements is suggested by the information in the drawing?

○ A. Both groups were armed with muskets.
○ B. Both groups traveled to the battle by canoe.
○ C. Champlain was the only Frenchman in the battle.
○ D. The men on the ground were only slightly wounded.

19. Which of these statements is supported by information in the passage?

○ A. No one was killed or wounded.
○ B. The Iroquois were better warriors.
○ C. Champlain fired first, in self-defense.
○ D. The Huron outnumbered the Iroquois.

Exploring the Essential Question

How did Europeans explore and establish settlements in the Americas?

Follow the directions to complete the item below.

20. Based on your knowledge about the lessons learned by the early settlers, consider the ideal location for a group of people to settle in the Americas. Write a paragraph describing the environment that would provide for a successful settlement.

    Your paragraph should include

    - a physical description of the environment, including resources, landscape, climate.
    - economic activities supported by the environment.
    - environmental conditions that provide protection for the settlers.

    Make sure to convey your ideas clearly, using standard English.

Creating a Colonial Sales Booth

Your group will create an exciting, informative sales booth to encourage people to settle in your colony. Your booth will include a poster, a musical jingle, and a sales presentation. Have your teacher initial each step as you complete it.

_____ **Step 1: Review the roles.** Make sure everyone knows the responsibilities for his or her role.

Advertising Director: You will lead the group during Step 2 to make sure everyone understands key historical information about your colony. During Step 5, you will lead the group to create a musical jingle for the sales presentation. As a member of Team A, you and the Copywriter will present your booth to your classmates.

Copywriter: You will lead the group during Step 3 to write a slogan and sentences describing your colony's best features. As a member of Team A, you and the Advertising Director will present your booth to your classmates.

Graphic Artist: You will lead the group during Step 4 to create the layout of the poster and visuals of your colony's key features. As a member of Team B, you and the Salesperson will present your booth to your classmates.

Salesperson: You will lead the group during Step 6 to create a sales presentation to convince others to settle in your colony. As a member of Team B, you and the Graphic Artist will present your booth to your classmates.

_____ **Step 2: Learn about your colony.** Take turns reading aloud about your colony in your book, including the list of information about your colony. The Advertising Director should make sure everyone completes the spoke diagram for your colony in the Reading Notes.

_____ **Step 3: Summarize your colony's best features.** Create a slogan for your poster that summarizes your colony's most outstanding feature—for example, "New Jersey: Land of Great Variety." Have the Copywriter record your slogan.

Then brainstorm at least five more features of your colony to include on your poster. Include features for each of these topics: Reasons for Settlement, Geography and Climate, Religion, and Government. Choose features that make the colony sound like an appealing place to live. Help the Copywriter write a sentence for each feature.

_____ **Step 4: Create a poster highlighting your colony's best features.** Your poster should be visually appealing, informative, and creative. It must have your slogan, the sentences from Step 3, and at least four visuals of your colony's best features. Have the Graphic Artist quickly sketch the layout of the poster and the four visuals. Then work together to create your poster.

_____ **Step 5: Brainstorm ideas for a musical jingle.** The sales presentation will include a musical jingle that promotes your colony's best features. You may create your own tune or use the tune of a well-known song. Help the Advertising Director write a two- to four-line jingle.

_____ **Step 6: Create a sales presentation.** Each team from your group will have three minutes to present your colony to the booth's visitors. The presentation should be educational and entertaining. It should also refer to your poster and include the musical jingle. Determine the order in which you will talk about each topic, when you will sing the jingle, and anything else you might do to highlight your colony's best features. The Salesperson should outline these main ideas on a separate sheet of paper.

_____ **Step 7: Rehearse the sales presentation.** Have Team A and Team B take turns rehearsing the sales presentation and jingle. The observing team should make sure the presentation is easy to follow, interesting to watch, and lasts no more than three minutes.

Chapter 3 Assessment

Mastering the Content

Fill in the circle next to the best answer.

1. Which of these documents is most similar to the Mayflower Compact?
   - ○ A. the Bible
   - ○ B. the Constitution
   - ○ C. the Gettysburg Address
   - ○ D. the Emancipation Proclamation

2. How did Roger Williams's colony of Providence differ from the Puritan colony of Massachusetts?
   - ○ A. Enslaved people were made free.
   - ○ B. Only religious men were allowed to vote.
   - ○ C. American Indians were considered enemies.
   - ○ D. People of different religious beliefs were welcomed.

3. The actions and beliefs of the Quakers of Pennsylvania predicted which of these events?
   - ○ A. the failure of Roanoke
   - ○ B. the Mayflower journey
   - ○ C. the American Revolution
   - ○ D. the French and Indian War

4. Which of these colonies offered the most freedom for the people who lived there?
   - ○ A. Georgia
   - ○ B. Virginia
   - ○ C. Pennsylvania
   - ○ D. Massachusetts

5. Which of these features made the Southern colonies unique?
   - ○ A. self-government
   - ○ B. religious freedom
   - ○ C. general assemblies
   - ○ D. tobacco plantations

6. James Oglethorpe intended that the Georgia colony be settled by
   - ○ A. English debtors.
   - ○ B. indentured servants.
   - ○ C. religious Separatists.
   - ○ D. wealthy businesspeople.

7. Why did Virginia replace indentured servants with African slaves?
   - ○ A. It was required by law.
   - ○ B. Africa was closer than Europe.
   - ○ C. Africans were more willing to work.
   - ○ D. It provided a permanent source of labor.

8. Which of these describes an indentured servant?
   - ○ A. Jonathon paid his debt to a farmer by working for him without pay.
   - ○ B. Samuel paid rent on his farm with a portion of his crops.
   - ○ C. Cecilia made and sold candles to wealthy landowners.
   - ○ D. Sarah was sold to a landowner and worked as a cook.

9. What did the New England colonies have in common?
   - ○ A. They were self-governing.
   - ○ B. They were settled by Puritans.
   - ○ C. They provided financial security.
   - ○ D. They provided religious freedom.

10. Which of these made the laws in most of the colonies?
    - ○ A. the church leaders
    - ○ B. the king of England
    - ○ C. the English governor
    - ○ D. the elected assembly

11. Why did people in the New England, Middle, and Southern colonies adapt different ways of life?
    - ○ A. People with specific skills settled in each area.
    - ○ B. The regions had different geographies and resources.
    - ○ C. The people all had different reasons for settling in North America.
    - ○ D. The leaders of the colonies decided how the people would earn a living.

12. Which generalization best sums up the founding of the English colonies?
    - ○ A. The English colonies were founded by Puritans, Quakers, and Catholics who wanted religious freedom.
    - ○ B. The English colonies were founded to provide a new start to poor people throughout Europe.
    - ○ C. The English colonies were founded by businesspeople who planned to make money by selling land to settlers.
    - ○ D. The English colonies were founded by people with various goals, from making money to following their faith.

13. Which of these best describes the environment of the New England colonies?
    - ○ A. long, hot summers and mild winters
    - ○ B. harsh winters and rocky, hilly land
    - ○ C. broad coastal plains and fertile soil
    - ○ D. broad rivers, swamps, and wetlands

14. How did the government of New York differ from the other colonies?
    - ○ A. It was self-governed.
    - ○ B. It was ruled by religious leaders.
    - ○ C. It was led by a powerful general assembly.
    - ○ D. It was ruled by a British-appointed governor.

15. Which of these colonies was most motivated by making a profit?
    - ○ A. Virginia
    - ○ B. Connecticut
    - ○ C. Pennsylvania
    - ○ D. Massachusetts

16. Which of these describes the Separatists?
    - ○ A. They were English soldiers.
    - ○ B. They shared religious beliefs.
    - ○ C. They were wealthy English investors.
    - ○ D. They shared a common occupation.

Applying Social Studies Skills

Use the map and your knowledge of history to answer the questions.

17. Which of the three colonial regions was most dependent upon the ocean for its economy?

Colonial America, 1770

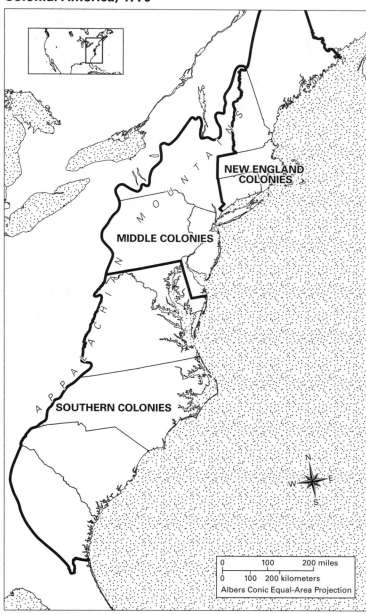

18. One colony was founded with the hope that it would prevent the Spanish from attacking the other colonies. Which region was this colony in?

19. Describe one effect that the Appalachian Mountains may have had on the 13 colonies.

Exploring the Essential Question

What were the similarities and differences among the colonies in North America?

Follow the directions to complete the item below.

20. Take on the role of a newspaper editor in colonial times. You will write three "want ads" describing the qualifications for settlers in those particular colonies. The first want ad is started for you. Fill in the blanks, and then create two more ads of your own for two different colonies. Your want ads should include

    • the name of the colony.
    • a description of the type of person welcome in the colony.
    • qualifications of a prospective colonist.
    • benefits that the colony offers.

    Also make sure to convey your ideas clearly, using standard English.

WANTED

William Penn is seeking Quakers in Pennsylvania. Must agree to live simply and treat everyone _____ . Must be willing to treat Indians _____ . Pennsylvania can offer you _____ , which will bring you prosperity and peace.

WANTED	**WANTED**

Analyzing Information About Life in the Colonies

Acting as investigative journalists, you and your partner will investigate life in the American colonies. You will travel to eight places to examine primary and secondary sources and uncover the truth about what life was really like in the colonies. Follow these steps to conduct your investigation:

Step 1: Go to one of the available placards, and examine the primary and secondary sources there. Discuss the questions on the placard with your partner.

Step 2: Locate the related section of Reading Notes in your Interactive Student Notebook. Record your answer to the Key Question in your Reading Notes. Make sure you give specific evidence from the placard.

Step 3: Ask your teacher to check your answer to the Key Question. Then read the corresponding section in your book and complete the Reading Notes for that section.

Step 4: Repeat Steps 1 to 3 with a new placard.

Chapter 4 Assessment

Mastering the Content

Fill in the circle next to the best answer.

1. Which of these English traditions was adopted in the 13 colonies?
   - ○ A. monarchy
   - ○ B. Parliament
   - ○ C. political parties
   - ○ D. self-government

2. How did the Great Awakening in the 1730s prepare the colonists for the American Revolution?
   - ○ A. It established an army.
   - ○ B. It created anti-colonial sentiment.
   - ○ C. It required colonists to pay heavy taxes.
   - ○ D. It encouraged the ideals of liberty and equality.

3. What was an effect of Magna Carta in England?
   - ○ A. It limited the power of the king.
   - ○ B. It established a democratic government.
   - ○ C. It allowed Parliament to impose taxes.
   - ○ D. It established a Bill of Rights for the citizens.

4. What was a main goal of education for students in the New England colonies?
   - ○ A. to be able to read the Bible
   - ○ B. to become political leaders
   - ○ C. to be prepared to attend college
   - ○ D. to become wealthy landowners

5. How did the establishment of Parliament strengthen the rights of English citizens?
   - ○ A. Citizens were able to choose the monarch.
   - ○ B. The king was denied power over citizens.
   - ○ C. Citizens determined whether laws would be passed.
   - ○ D. Laws were made by representatives of the citizens.

6. Which right did the English Bill of Rights provide?
   - ○ A. to petition the king
   - ○ B. to determine national holidays
   - ○ C. to choose punishments for crimes
   - ○ D. to choose the kind of school children would attend

7. Why was the English Bill of Rights important to the colonists?
   - ○ A. It defined crimes and punishments.
   - ○ B. It spelled out what was due to the colonists as English citizens.
   - ○ C. It gave the colonists the ability to choose members of Parliament.
   - ○ D. It ended the king's power to appoint colonial governors.

8. The Middle Passage refers to
   - ○ A. the ocean crossing of the slaves.
   - ○ B. the route taken to reach New York.
   - ○ C. a step in climbing the social ladder.
   - ○ D. a system of trade between the colonies.

9. Which of these is true about slavery in the colonies?
- ○ A. Laws were written to abolish slavery.
- ○ B. It expanded throughout the colonies.
- ○ C. It was limited to the Southern colonies.
- ○ D. Northern slaves were freed and returned to Africa.

10. Which belief spurred the Great Awakening?
- ○ A. People have lost their faith.
- ○ B. Farm life is better than city life.
- ○ C. Women are not as educated as men.
- ○ D. Success comes from making money.

11. What slowed the growth of public education in the Middle Colonies?
- ○ A. lack of materials
- ○ B. discipline problems
- ○ C. religious differences
- ○ D. little interest in education

12. Which of these shows the chronological order of the founding of these concepts?
- ○ A. Parliament, English Bill of Rights, Magna Carta, Great Awakening
- ○ B. Magna Carta, Great Awakening, English Bill of Rights, Parliament
- ○ C. English Bill of Rights, Parliament, Magna Carta
- ○ D. Magna Carta, Parliament, English Bill of Rights, Great Awakening

13. What event became known as the Glorious Revolution?
- ○ A. Slaves rebelled and escaped to freedom.
- ○ B. African leaders ended slave trade with Europeans.
- ○ C. Parliament was formed with the co-operation of the king.
- ○ D. The king was overthrown and Parliament retained lawmaking powers.

14. In which way were colonial public schools like the public schools of today?
- ○ A. The schools taught reading and writing.
- ○ B. The schools were paid for with tax dollars.
- ○ C. Teachers were hired by the parents.
- ○ D. All children were required to attend.

15. How did a colonist achieve a higher class in colonial society?
- ○ A. by making a lot of money
- ○ B. by going to church regularly
- ○ C. by working for a landowner
- ○ D. by inheriting an important title

16. What were the expectations of English colonists in America?
- ○ A. They expected to be governed by the English king.
- ○ B. They expected the same rights as English citizens.
- ○ C. They expected to denounce their English citizenship.
- ○ D. They expected to be able to choose the leader of Parliament.

Applying Social Studies Skills

Use the illustration and your knowledge of history to answer the questions.

17. Which of these colonies is most likely pictured in this illustration?
○ A. Georgia
○ B. Virginia
○ C. Rhode Island
○ D. Massachusetts

18. Briefly explain why you believe the colony you chose is shown in the illustration.

19. List one aspect of colonial life that can be observed in the illustration.

Exploring the Essential Question

What was life really like in the colonies?

Follow the directions to complete the item below.

20. Suppose you recently moved to the colonies from England. You want to write a letter to your family in England describing your life in the colonies. In your letter, do the following:

   - Focus on daily activities, including work, leisure, and family. (Decide whether you live in the city or on a farm.)

   - Include your views on recent news in the colonies regarding public education and slavery.

   - Ask questions of your family regarding the English Bill of Rights and the work of Parliament.

   Also make sure to convey your ideas clearly, using standard English.

Unit 1 Timeline Challenge Cards

Humans Reach North America
10,000 or more years ago

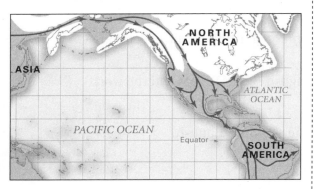

The first humans, likely Siberian hunter families, reach the Americas by crossing a wide bridge of land between Asia and North America called Beringia.

Magna Carta
1215

King John of England signs Magna Carta, limiting his power and giving more rights to the English people.

American Indian Culture Flourishes
1400s

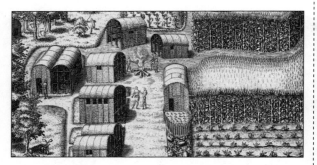

One to two million American Indians live in North America, north of Mexico. American Indian groups have distinct beliefs, customs, foods, dwellings, and clothing.

Columbus Sails to the Americas
1492

Christopher Columbus sails to the Americas and explores the islands in what is now called the Caribbean Sea.

Slave Trade
1500s

As part of the Atlantic slave trade, Africans are brought to the Americas and sold into slavery. Slavery becomes a way of life in many American colonies.

Jamestown Founded
1607

Jamestown becomes the first permanent English colony in North America. Despite initial hardships, the colony survives and flourishes.

Mayflower Compact
1620

Pilgrims from England sail to the Americas seeking to establish "a perfect society." During their voyage, they sign the Mayflower Compact, which describes how they will govern themselves.

Providence Founded
1636

Roger Williams breaks from the Puritans and establishes the settlement of Providence, which eventually becomes part of the colony of Rhode Island.

Pennsylvania Founded
1681

Seeking religious freedom for the Quakers, William Penn establishes the colony of Pennsylvania and promises that people of all faiths will be treated equally.

English Bill of Rights
1689

Prince William and his wife Mary sign the English Bill of Rights, strengthening the rights of the English people and the power of colonial assemblies.

Salem Witch Trials
1692

Fear of witchcraft erupts among the Puritans in Salem, Massachusetts. Nineteen young women are put on trial and executed.

Great Awakening
1730s and 1740s

The Great Awakening revives religion in the colonies and spreads the ideas of liberty and equality.

Role Cards of Historical Figures

Joseph Brant: Loyalist

You are Joseph Brant, born in Ohio in 1742. A Mohawk Indian and a leader of the Iroquois nations, you went to school in Connecticut, where you learned English. You are loyal to Great Britain partly because you joined the Church of England in 1763. You fought with the British in the French and Indian War. Your brother-in-law is Sir William Johnson, a Loyalist and a wealthy landowner.

In 1775, you went to England, where you were treated like a celebrity. You met the king and told him that the Mohawks are a free people and that you believe they must remain so. The king agreed. He assured you that the Mohawks, as long as they fought against the colonists, would be given land in Canada when the conflict with the colonists was over.

Swearing loyalty to Great Britain, you pledged to support that nation with 1,500 warriors. During the war, you will lead four of the six Iroquois nations against the colonists.

Thomas Hutchinson: Loyalist

You are Governor Thomas Hutchinson of Massachusetts, a Loyalist. Although you do not totally agree with Parliament's decisions to tax the colonies, you believe that Parliament has the right to rule the colonies and to pass laws affecting them. You believe that without British rule, there would be a total breakdown of government in America. Therefore, you loyally enforce Parliament's laws in Massachusetts.

You were born to wealthy landowners in Boston. You are a lawyer, historian, and author. At the time of the Stamp Act, you were the chief justice (judge) of Massachusetts. Although you opposed the Stamp Act, you ruled against the colonists in several court cases because you believe in British law and British rule.

You are a leading Loyalist in America. You try to limit the influence of the Patriots. You want to restrict town meetings. When Samuel Adams published articles in the *Boston Gazette* attacking the Stamp Act, you tried to bring charges of sedition against him. (Seditious acts encourage people to disobey lawful authority.) You also tried to enforce the Tea Act, which led to the Boston Tea Party.

Peter Van Schaack: Loyalist

You are Peter Van Schaack, a wealthy landowner from New York. You believe that the colonies are part of the British Empire and that all laws passed by Parliament apply to the colonies.

At first, you supported the colonists' complaints. However, you later changed your mind. You believe that the colonies need Great Britain to survive. You argue that having the protection of Great Britain's military, as well as Great Britain's economic strength, serves the general good of the colonies.

You believe that the colonies cannot function without British rule. You also believe that Parliament has the right to tax all British subjects, including the colonists. If the colonies gain independence, you argue, they will only fight among themselves to determine their new form of government and who will rule.

Rebecca Franks: Loyalist

You are Rebecca Franks of Philadelphia. You believe that it is in Americans' best interest to remain under British rule. You do not share all of the Patriots' political beliefs, and you think some of their concerns are exaggerated. However, you do believe that the colonies should be given some say in how they are governed.

Your father, David Franks, is a businessman. He provided supplies to the British army in the years before the war. Your life is filled with parties and social events. You are admired by all—Loyalists and Patriots alike—because of your wit, beauty, and charm.

John Adams: Patriot

You are John Adams of Massachusetts. You are best known as a leader of the Patriots. You have won great respect among other Patriots since joining the rebellion. Many colonists, however, are put off by your boastful attitude.

You did not always believe in rebellion. After you graduated from Harvard College and became a lawyer, your cousin Samuel Adams convinced you to join the resistance against Great Britain as a legal adviser. You opposed Parliament's taxing the colonies without colonial representation. However, you also supported English law and were not interested in independence.

After the Boston Massacre in 1770, you changed your mind. You became convinced that the colonies must fight for independence. Still, you defended the British soldiers charged with murder after the Boston Massacre because you believe in justice under the law.

After being elected to the Massachusetts House of Representatives, you became more and more critical of Britain's efforts to tax the colonists. When Bostonians were forced to house British troops after the Boston Tea Party, you called a meeting of Patriots to tell them not to pay for the tea that had been dumped into the harbor.

During the First and Second Continental Congresses, you will call on the delegates 23 times to discuss independence. You will recommend establishing a continental government to represent all the colonies.

Patrick Henry: Patriot

You are Patrick Henry of Virginia, a lawyer and one of the first colonists to call for independence from Great Britain. You were an elected member of Virginia's lawmaking body, the House of Burgesses. You resigned so that you could devote your time to fighting Great Britain's attempts to tax the colonies. You believe that these taxes are unfair because the colonists have no representatives in Parliament.

You are constantly telling Americans that they will never be free unless the colonies become independent. As long as the colonies are part of the British Empire, you argue, colonists will be second-class citizens with no political rights. You also are responsible for forming the Virginia militia.

You are most famous for a speech in which you addressed fellow Virginians who were opposed to rebellion. "I know not what course others may take," you declared. "But as for me, give me liberty or give me death!"

Benjamin Franklin: Patriot

You are Benjamin Franklin of Philadelphia, one of America's best-known and most beloved statesmen. You are an inventor, a scholar, and a civic leader. In 1748, at the age of 42, you retired to devote yourself to civic projects. You were responsible for organizing Philadelphia's first police force, the University of Pennsylvania, and the city's first hospital.

In 1757, you were sent to Great Britain to represent Pennsylvania's interests in England. Eventually, you became the representative for New Jersey, Georgia, and Massachusetts as well. In 1765, you wrote to the angry colonists and told them to have patience toward the Stamp Act. Then you tried to persuade Parliament to repeal (cancel) the act. You believe that Parliament's ability to conduct business with the colonies depends on the colonists' respect for the British government. You warned Parliament that if the Stamp Act were not withdrawn, the colonists would lose all respect for Great Britain.

You were alarmed when the Stamp Act was replaced by the Townshend Acts. You urged the colonists to boycott (refuse to buy) British goods until these taxes were withdrawn. When the British tried to bribe you to persuade the colonists to end their opposition, you told them that your patriotism has no price tag. In 1775, you returned to Philadelphia and were elected to the Pennsylvania Assembly. You now believe the colonies should declare independence, and you openly work for the cause of rebellion.

Thomas Jefferson: Patriot

You are Thomas Jefferson of Virginia. You are a lawyer and a brilliant thinker and writer. After hearing Patrick Henry declare "Give me liberty or give me death!" you became committed to rebellion against Great Britain. You firmly believe in democracy and do not want to be governed by Parliament without someone representing your interests. You convinced the Virginia lawmaking body, the House of Burgesses, to pass a resolution that criticized taxation without representation.

You are generally respected and well liked by all colonists—Patriots and Loyalists alike—because you are charming, intelligent, and a humanitarian. You support religious freedom and public education.

You strongly support the radicals in New England and oppose the British occupation of Boston. You tell your fellow Virginians that the occupation is not just an attack on Boston. "An attack on any one colony should be considered an attack on the whole," you say. When the British closed the port of Boston, you called on all Virginians to support their fellow colonists by praying and fasting (going without food) until the port was reopened.

Mercy Otis Warren: Patriot

You are Mercy Otis Warren of Boston, a well-known historian and author. You believe that the colonies should resist the "strong hand of foreign domination." You are convinced that the time has come for the colonies to break their ties to Britain.

You write articles for the *Boston Gazette* that criticize Loyalists, calling them traitors. Your writings also attack Great Britain for sending troops to Boston. History, you say, teaches that a standing army is the tool of tyrants (leaders who abuse power).

You also write articles criticizing Massachusetts governor Thomas Hutchinson. You say that Hutchinson has opened the way to rebellion by enforcing Great Britain's unjust laws.

The Earl of Effingham: Neutralist

You are the Earl of Effingham, a member of Parliament. You are a Neutralist. You believe that the coming conflict will have a negative impact on both Great Britain and the colonies.

You tell Parliament that you are devoted to Great Britain and to the king. You say that you will sacrifice your life and your wealth for the cause of defending England against foreign attack. At the same time, you do not believe it is right for Parliament to tax British citizens in America when they have no representation in Parliament.

James Allen: Neutralist

You are James Allen, a landowner from Philadelphia. You are a Neutralist. You believe that the rebellion will keep you from collecting rent from your tenants. You fear you will become poor because of the war.

You are angry because the colonial and British armies are both demanding that you provide them with supplies. The Continental army pays you with Continental dollars, which are almost worthless. The British do not pay you at all. In addition, you are upset because basic products such as meat, butter, and cheese have tripled in price.

You believe that the conflict has caused a total breakdown in government and law. You want some type of government to protect the rights of British citizens in the colonies.

Richard Henderson: Neutralist

You are Richard Henderson, a land merchant from Kentucky. You are a Neutralist. You believe that the Patriots are mostly wealthy gentlemen who have access to the courts, participate in elections, and read newspapers. These few people, you fear, will impose their will on Americans if they win the war.

However, you also believe that the British have not dealt fairly with the colonists. You say that they allowed the first settlers to leave England and establish themselves in North America without having to obey British law. The British government, you argue, allowed colonists to trade without taxing them. You also believe that the British government is not being fair in taxing the colonies to pay for debts from the French and Indian War.

Felix Holbrook: Neutralist

You are Felix Holbrook, a slave living in Boston. You are a Neutralist. You have placed an ad in a Boston newspaper asking for permission to buy your freedom. Your ad praises colonists for taking a stand against those trying to enslave them. You say you understand their feelings and their desire to fight for political and religious freedom. You ask for the privilege of earning money to buy your own freedom and return to your homeland in Africa.

"Give us that ample relief which, as men, we have a natural right to," you write. You stress that you wish to gain your freedom by peaceful and lawful means.

Representing Your Historical Figure

Follow these steps to prepare to represent your historical figure.

Step 1: As a group, read your role card. Highlight your occupation and important beliefs, arguments, opinions, and criticisms. Do not highlight your specific reactions to future events.

Step 2: Prepare a short introduction of yourself as your historical figure by completing the three statements below. Summarize the information you highlighted on your role card to complete the third statement in one or two sentences.

My name is _____.

I am _____ *(your occupation) and a* _____
(Patriot/Loyalist/Neutralist).

I believe

Step 3: When your teacher calls on your group, have one group member stand and present your historical figure to the class. Do not read your introduction.

Preparing for the Colonial Town Meetings

Follow these steps to prepare for the colonial town meetings.

Colonial Town Meeting 1

1. In your group, evaluate the actions of the British by completing these sentences:
   - *We believe the Proclamation of 1763 is fair/unfair because . . .*
   - *We believe the Stamp Act was fair/unfair and its repeal is fair/unfair because . . .*
   - *We believe the Quartering Act is fair/unfair because . . .*

2. How should you and your fellow colonists choose to respond to the British government at this point in time?
   - Comply (obey without question)
   - Oppose (protest even if unwilling to declare independence)
   - Rebel (declare independence)

3. Prepare a spokesperson (someone who has not addressed the class yet) to defend your position on this question: *At this point in time, should American colonists rebel against the British government? If not, what should we do?*

Colonial Town Meeting 2

1. In your group, evaluate the actions of the British by completing these sentences:
   - *We believe the Townshend Acts were fair/unfair and their repeal is fair/unfair because . . .*
   - *The Boston Massacre was/was not justified because . . .*

2. How should you and your fellow colonists choose to respond to the British government at this point in time?
   - Comply (obey without question)
   - Oppose (protest even if unwilling to declare independence)
   - Rebel (declare independence)

Colonial Town Meeting 3

1. In your group, evaluate the actions of the British by completing these sentences:

    *   *We believe the Tea Act is fair/unfair because . . .*
    *   *We believe the Intolerable Acts are fair/unfair because . . .*

2. How should you and your fellow colonists choose to respond to the British government at this point in time?

    *   Comply (obey without question)
    *   Oppose (protest even if unwilling to declare independence)
    *   Rebel (declare independence)

3. Prepare a spokesperson (someone who has not yet addressed the class) to defend your position on this question: *At this point in time, should American colonists rebel against the British government? If not, what should we do?*

Colonial Town Meeting 4

1. In your group, evaluate the actions of the British by completing this sentence:

    *   *The battles at Lexington and Concord were/were not justified because . . .*

2. How should you and your fellow colonists choose to respond to the British government at this point in time?

    *   Comply (obey without question)
    *   Oppose (protest even if unwilling to declare independence)
    *   Rebel (declare independence)

Chapter 5 Assessment

Mastering the Content
Fill in the circle next to the best answer.

1. Before 1760, which statement **best** describes the colonies?
   - ○ A. The colonies had assemblies that passed laws.
   - ○ B. The colonies had representation in Parliament.
   - ○ C. The colonies were united into one government.
   - ○ D. The colonies depended upon the British government.

2. Which of these groups gained territory in North America as a result of the French and Indian War?
   - ○ A. Spain
   - ○ B. France
   - ○ C. Great Britain
   - ○ D. American Indians

3. Which of these groups benefited from the Proclamation of 1763?
   - ○ A. African slaves
   - ○ B. British soldiers
   - ○ C. American Indians
   - ○ D. American colonists

4. Which of these was a result of the French and Indian War?
   - ○ A. The British government had a large war debt.
   - ○ B. The colonists were given their independence.
   - ○ C. The British government stayed out of colonial politics.
   - ○ D. The colonists were free to move west of the Appalachians.

5. Which group formed the Sons of Liberty?
   - ○ A. Patriots
   - ○ B. Loyalists
   - ○ C. British soldiers
   - ○ D. American Indians

6. The name Boston Massacre was given to the events of March 5, 1770, in order to
   - ○ A. create anti-British sentiment.
   - ○ B. create trouble for the colonists.
   - ○ C. warn of a deadly disease in the city.
   - ○ D. describe the truth about what happened.

7. Which of these belongs in place of the question mark in the diagram below?
   - ○ A. Proclamation of 1763
   - ○ B. French and Indian War
   - ○ C. boycott of British goods
   - ○ D. expansion of the British Empire

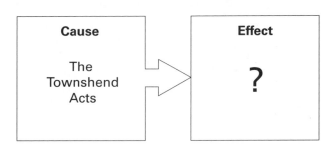

8. What did the colonists resent **most** about the Stamp Act?
   - ○ A. They did not believe in any form of taxation.
   - ○ B. They had no representatives to vote on the tax.
   - ○ C. People in Great Britain did not have to pay taxes.
   - ○ D. People in Great Britain were taxed only on property.

9. What was Great Britain's response to the Boston Tea Party?

○ A. the Stamp Act
○ B. the Intolerable Acts
○ C. the Boston Massacre
○ D. the Proclamation of 1763

10. In which way did Great Britain increase its control of the colonies?

○ A. It took away colonists' land.
○ B. It required that colonists pay taxes.
○ C. It demanded that colonists join the army.
○ D. It forced colonists to work for the government.

11. What was a goal of the First Continental Congress?

○ A. to declare war on Great Britain
○ B. to find a solution to the conflicts with Great Britain
○ C. to create taxes that would be acceptable to the Americans
○ D. to bring representatives from Great Britain and America together

12. Which of these **best** describes how the colonists viewed themselves in 1774?

○ A. They saw themselves as united Americans.
○ B. They saw themselves as dependent on the king.
○ C. They saw themselves as citizens of their individual colonies.
○ D. They saw themselves as united under the British government.

13. How did Parliament respond to the colonists' protests against the Stamp Act?

○ A. They repealed the Stamp Act.
○ B. They increased the tax on paper.
○ C. They refused to sell stamps to the colonists.
○ D. They arrested those who complained about the Stamp Act.

14. How did many of the Loyalists view the Patriots?

○ A. as brave soldiers
○ B. as foreign invaders
○ C. as ungrateful rebels
○ D. as agreeable neighbors

15. Which of these did the colonists consider an act of tyranny?

○ A. the Boston Tea Party
○ B. the Proclamation of 1763
○ C. the French and Indian War
○ D. the First Continental Congress

16. What became evident when the colonists and British troops clashed at Lexington and Concord?

○ A. The British soldiers were fearful of the colonial militia.
○ B. The British troops were eager to start a war with the colonies.
○ C. The colonial militia was no match for the well-trained British troops.
○ D. The colonists were willing to fight for the right to govern themselves.

Applying Social Studies Skills

Use the two engravings and your knowledge of history to answer the questions.

17. To which of the following events are the two Paul Revere engravings referring?

○ A. Boston Tea Party
○ B. Boston Massacre
○ C. Proclamation of 1763
○ D. French and Indian War

18. Look at the men who are shooting in the first engraving. Which group of people do these men represent?

○ A. British
○ B. Patriots
○ C. Loyalists
○ D. Parliament

19. What reaction is Paul Revere trying to stir up in the colonists through his engravings? Cite words and other details in the engravings to support your answer.

Exploring the Essential Question

When is it necessary for citizens to rebel against their government?

Follow the directions to complete the item below.

20. Suppose you were giving a speech at a Massachusetts town meeting in 1774. You are trying to persuade the community to join the rebellion against British rule of the colonies. Write a short persuasive speech that describes

   - how life in the colonies has changed since the British have taken a greater interest in the colonies.
   - at least one act of the British government that has denied colonial freedom.
   - at least one right that has been taken away due to British actions or policies.
   - an action to be taken by the colonists.

   Make sure to convey your ideas clearly, using standard English.

Analyzing Excerpts from the Declaration of Independence

Part 1 You will receive a card with excerpts from the Declaration of Independence written in modern language. Work with your partner to match those modern excerpts with the actual excerpts from the Declaration in the chart.

Have your teacher check your answers. If your answers are correct, copy the modern versions into the chart. Then get a new card and repeat the process.

Excerpts from the Declaration of Independence	Excerpts in Modern Language
Excerpt 1: When in the Course of human events it becomes necessary for one people to dissolve the political bands which have connected them with another . . . a decent respect to the opinions of mankind requires that they should declare the causes which impel them to the separation.	Principle of government: ___
Excerpt 2: We hold these truths to be self-evident, that all men are created equal, that they are endowed by their Creator with certain unalienable Rights, that among these are Life, Liberty and the pursuit of Happiness.	Principle of government: ___
Excerpt 3: That to secure these rights, Governments are instituted among Men, deriving their just powers from the consent of the governed.	Principle of government: ___
Excerpt 4: That whenever any Form of Government becomes destructive of these ends, it is the Right of the People to alter or to abolish it, and to institute new Government.	Principle of government: ___
Excerpt 5: The history of the present King of Great Britain is a history of repeated injuries and usurpations, all having in direct object the establishment of an absolute Tyranny over these States.	Principle of government: ___
Excerpt 6: In every stage of these Oppressions We have Petitioned for Redress in the most humble terms: Our repeated Petitions have been answered only by repeated injury. A Prince whose character is thus marked by every act which may define a Tyrant, is unfit to be the ruler.	Principle of government: ___
Excerpt 7: These United Colonies are, and of Right ought to be Free and Independent States; that they are Absolved from all Allegiance to the British Crown, and that all political connection between them and the State of Great Britain, is and ought to be totally dissolved.	Principle of government: ___

Part 2

1. The following four principles of government are used in the Declaration
    of Independence to make the argument for independence. Fill in the
    missing words.

    Principle 1 All _____ are created equal.

    Principle 2 All people have basic _____ that cannot be taken away.

    Principle 3 The government gets its power to make decisions and protect rights

    from the _____ .

    Principle 4 When the government does not protect the _____

    of the people, the _____ have the right to

    _____ or _____ the government.

2. Identify which principle of government is expressed in each of the seven
    excerpts from the Declaration of Independence. Excerpts may express more
    than one principle.

    Write the numbers of the principles in the chart. Also underline the portions
    of the excerpts that support your choices.

Excerpts in Modern Language

A We now consider ourselves to be an independent country. We have no more loyalty to Great Britain and they no longer have the power to rule over us.

B When a government takes away the rights of citizens, the citizens have the right to change the government or create a new one.

C All people have some basic rights that cannot be taken away. Liberty is one of those rights.

D The current ruler of Great Britain has repeatedly interfered with colonists' rights, sometimes even taking them away. He has ruled unfairly over the American colonies.

E Governments are formed to make sure people's rights are protected. The power to govern comes from the people.

F Every time we colonists felt we were being treated unfairly, we wrote the king. He answered by treating us more unfairly. A ruler who abuses his power should not rule us.

G When people break away from a country to form a new nation, they should explain why they are doing it.

Four Principles of Government in the Declaration of Independence

Principle 1

All people are created equal.

Principle 2

All people have basic rights that cannot be taken away.

Principle 3

The government gets its power to make decisions and to protect rights from the people.

Principle 4

When the government does not protect the rights of the people, the people have the right to change or remove the government.

Writing an Essay About the Principles in the Declaration of Independence

Write an essay discussing how well the United States is upholding the principles of the Declaration of Independence. Use your Reading Notes, Student Handout 6A, your personal experiences and opinions, and your knowledge of current events for information to write your essay.

Your essay must use correct grammar and spelling and include these things:

- A brief introduction in which you clearly state your thesis. Your thesis will answer this question: *How well is the United States upholding the principles of the Declaration of Independence?*

- Two paragraphs defending your thesis. In each paragraph, give and explain a piece of evidence in support of your thesis. This evidence can be drawn from current events or your own life experience. Clearly connect each piece of evidence to one of the four principles of government found in the Declaration of Independence.

- A short conclusion in which you summarize your thesis and the evidence you used to support it.

- At least one excerpt from the Declaration of Independence.

Also make sure to do the following:

- Express your ideas clearly, so the reader will understand them.
- Verify that each detail in your essay supports your thesis.

Chapter 6 Assessment

Mastering the Content

Fill in the circle next to the best answer.

1. Which of these describes the mood in the colonies immediately following the events at Lexington and Concord?
   - ○ A. Most of the colonists were reluctant to start a war.
   - ○ B. Most of the colonists were eager to declare war against the British.
   - ○ C. Most of the colonists sided with the Loyalists against the Patriots.
   - ○ D. Most of the colonists wanted to move to Great Britain.

2. The Continental army was composed of
   - ○ A. troops from all the colonies.
   - ○ B. troops from throughout Great Britain.
   - ○ C. only troops from the New England colonies.
   - ○ D. only troops from Virginia and Massachusetts.

3. Patrick Henry gave a famous speech that ended with the words "give me liberty, or give me death!" With which group did he identify himself?
   - ○ A. Patriots
   - ○ B. Loyalists
   - ○ C. British citizens
   - ○ D. members of Parliament

4. Which of these **best** describes the outcome of the Battle of Bunker Hill?
   - ○ A. The British won decisively.
   - ○ B. The militia won by a narrow margin.
   - ○ C. The militia surrendered to the British.
   - ○ D. The British won but suffered many losses.

5. Why was George Washington chosen to be a military leader?
   - ○ A. He had experience.
   - ○ B. He wanted the role.
   - ○ C. He was very wealthy.
   - ○ D. He was highly educated.

6. What effect did *Common Sense* have in the colonies?
   - ○ A. It instilled fear of war in the colonists.
   - ○ B. It convinced the colonies to remain loyal to Great Britain.
   - ○ C. It persuaded many colonists that America should be independent.
   - ○ D. It petitioned the king to end the quarrel between the colonies and Great Britain.

7. Why was the Declaration of Independence written?
   - ○ A. to start the American Revolution
   - ○ B. to offer a peace settlement to Great Britain
   - ○ C. to instruct how a country wins its freedom
   - ○ D. to explain why the colonies were separating from Great Britain

8. In a draft of the Declaration of Independence, Jefferson charged the king with violating the "sacred rights of life and liberty . . . of a distant people [by] carrying them into slavery." This passage was removed for all of these reasons **except**
   - ○ A. it might lead to demands to free slaves.
   - ○ B. it was an unimportant issue in the colonies.
   - ○ C. it was unfair to blame the king for enslaving Africans.
   - ○ D. it might offend merchants who profited from the slave trade.

9. According to Thomas Jefferson, the power to rule comes from

    ○ A. God.
    ○ B. the king.
    ○ C. Parliament.
    ○ D. the citizens.

10. Why did Thomas Jefferson say that King George III was an unfit ruler?

    ○ A. He was not born in Great Britain.
    ○ B. He denied the colonists their rights.
    ○ C. He was not elected by Parliament.
    ○ D. He lived far away from the colonies.

11. How do natural rights, as described in the Declaration of Independence, differ from other rights?

    ○ A. People are born with natural rights.
    ○ B. People can vote to choose natural rights.
    ○ C. Natural rights are given only to citizens.
    ○ D. Natural rights come from the government.

12. Look at the timeline.

May 1775	June 1775	March 1776	July 1776
Second Continental Congress meets	Battle of Bunker Hill fought	Seige of Boston ends	**?**

Which of these belongs in place of the question mark on the timeline?

    ○ A. *Common Sense* published
    ○ B. Olive Branch Petition sent
    ○ C. American Revolution ends
    ○ D. Declaration of Independence signed

13. What was the purpose of the Olive Branch Petition?

    ○ A. to persuade British troops to leave Boston
    ○ B. to encourage colonists to join the army
    ○ C. to convince Parliament to repeal the Stamp Act
    ○ D. to ask King George to make peace with the colonies

14. Which of these shows cooperation on the part of the colonies?

    ○ A. They came together to form one army.
    ○ B. The Loyalists and Patriots made peace.
    ○ C. They all believed in the goal of independence.
    ○ D. They all opposed the Declaration of Independence.

15. What decision was made at the Second Continental Congress?

    ○ A. to form an army
    ○ B. to make a gesture of peace
    ○ C. to declare war on Great Britain
    ○ D. to demand a repeal of the Tea Act

16. To Great Britain, the signing of the Declaration of Independence was

    ○ A. an act of loyalty.
    ○ B. an act of treason.
    ○ C. an act of bravery.
    ○ D. an act of insanity.

Applying Social Studies Skills

Use the map and your knowledge of history to answer these questions.

Triangular Trade and the Enslavement of Africans

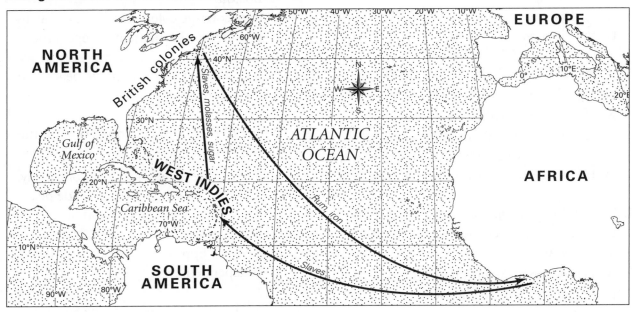

17. What were slaves traded for in the West Indies?

18. What was shipped from the British colonies to Africa?

19. Who benefited from the trade shown on the map?

Exploring the Essential Question

What principles of government are expressed in the Declaration of Independence?

Follow the directions to complete the item below.

20. The Declaration of Independence states that the purpose of government is to secure and protect the natural-born rights of citizens: the rights to life, liberty, and the pursuit of happiness. Write a three-paragraph essay that answers these questions:

   • What did Thomas Jefferson mean by the rights to life, liberty, and the pursuit of happiness?

   • How does our government protect our rights to life, liberty, and the pursuit of happiness?

   • What actions can our government take to better protect these rights or to assure that all U.S. citizens have these rights?

   Make sure to convey your ideas clearly, using standard English.

Procedures for Rounds 1 to 6 of Capture the Flag

Round 1
Step 1: Prepare teams for the first round of the game.

- Have the Red team stand in a line and warm up by stretching and jogging in place. Tell the Blue team not to do anything. ***Historical analogy:*** *The British military was better trained than the American forces.*

- Move half the Red team ten yards from the playing field. Tell these students they can enter the game only when you tell them to. ***Historical analogy:*** *British reinforcements and supplies had to travel across the Atlantic Ocean.*

- Tell the White team to root for the Blue team. ***Historical analogy:*** *France sent financial aid and supplies to the Americans early in the war.*

Ask the White team, *Who do you think will win? Why?*

Step 2: Have students play for approximately two minutes. Do not allow the other half of the Red team to enter the game during this round. Blow the whistle to end the round before the Red team can capture the Blue team's flag.

Step 3: Allow students one minute to rest, and permit Red and Blue players who are not currently playing the game to enter. Have the remainder of the Red team enter the game, and allow any students who have been tagged to reenter the game.

Round 2
Step 1: Prepare teams for the second round of the game.

- Tell the Blue team they will receive a prize if their team wins the game. Do not offer the Red team a prize for winning. ***Historical analogy:*** *The Declaration of Independence increased the motivation to win for most Americans.*

- Tell one student on the Blue team that even if the Blue team wins, you cannot guarantee that he or she will receive the prize offered other members of the Blue team. Give that student the opportunity to switch to the Red team. ***Historical analogy:*** *African Americans wondered whether the equality promised in the Declaration of Independence would apply to them. Many doubted it would and chose to fight on the British side. Others hoped they would be treated equally and chose to fight on the American side.*

Ask the White team, *Who do you think will win? Why?*

Step 2: Have students play for approximately two minutes. Blow the whistle to end the round before the Red team can capture the Blue team's flag.

Step 3: Allow students one minute to rest, and permit Red and Blue players who were tagged to reenter the game.

Round 3
Step 1: Prepare teams for the third round of the game.

- Call the Blue team aside and deliver a brief pep talk. Encourage the Blue team to keep a positive attitude, even though their situation looks difficult. Tell them, "These are the times that try men's souls." *Historical analogy: Thomas Paine's pamphlet* The Crisis *encouraged Patriots to keep fighting.*

- Add a second Blue flag that the Red team must capture. Tell both teams that the Red team must capture both flags to win. Tell the players on the Red team that one person may not capture both flags at once. *Historical analogy: American victories at Trenton and Princeton, in the Middle Colonies, showed the British that winning the war would be more difficult than they thought and boosted American morale.*

Ask the White team, *Who do you think will win? Why?*

Step 2: Have students play for approximately two minutes. Blow the whistle to end the round before the Red team can capture the Blue team's flag.

Step 3: Allow students one minute to rest, and permit Red and Blue players who were tagged to reenter the game.

Round 4
Step 1: Prepare teams for the fourth round of the game.

- Tell the Blue team that they do not have to capture the Red flag to win the game. They only have to keep the Red team from capturing all the Blue flags. *Historical analogy: Washington realized he did not have to defeat the British to win the war. He only needed to keep the British from defeating and capturing his army.*

- Call the Blue team aside and explain that if they can hold on for one more round, they will receive help. *Historical analogy: After the Americans won the Battle of Saratoga, the French promised to become active allies.*

- Allow one volunteer from the White team to join the Blue team. *Historical analogy: Several Europeans, such as Lafayette and von Steuben, volunteered to help the Americans.*

Ask the White team, *Who do you think will win? Why?*

Step 2: Have students play for approximately two minutes. Blow the whistle to end the round before the Red team can capture the Blue team's flag.

Step 3: Allow students one minute to rest, and permit Red and Blue players who were tagged to reenter the game.

Round 5

Step 1: Prepare teams for the fifth round of the game.

- Add a third Blue flag that the Red team must capture. Tell both teams that the Red team must capture all three Blue flags to win. Remind the players on the Red team that one person may not capture more than one flag at a time. *Historical analogy: Successful hit-and-run tactics used by the Americans in the Southern Colonies tired out the British forces.*

- Have the White team enter the game on the Blue team's side. Explain that if the Blue team wins, the White team will win a prize, too. *Historical analogy: France sent troops and naval support to America, which proved decisive at Yorktown.*

Step 2: Have students play for approximately two minutes. Blow the whistle to end the round before the Red team can capture the Blue team's flag.

Step 3: Allow students one minute to rest, and permit Red and Blue players who were tagged to reenter the game.

Round 6

Step 1: Ask the Red team members if they want to continue to play under the current rules. Allow Red team members to express their frustration over the way the rules have been changed to favor the Blue team. Expect many Red team members to say they are ready to quit and a few to adamantly argue to keep playing. *Historical analogy: After Yorktown, British popular support for the war decreased dramatically. King George and others, however, refused to accept defeat for months after Yorktown.*

Step 2: Declare the Blue team the winner. Have a representative from the Red team concede victory by shaking hands with representatives from the Blue and White teams. *Historical analogy: The Americans won the war.*

Step 3: Announce the terms of the end of the game. Have the Red team hand over its flag to the Blue team. Give the Blue and White teams their prizes. Finally, have the Blue team captain promise the Red team that Red team members will be treated with respect even though they lost the game. *Historical analogy: The Treaty of Paris ended the war. By the terms of the treaty, Great Britain withdrew its forces and recognized American independence. America promised that it would not seize any additional property from Loyalists.*

Simile for the Continental Army's Victory

The Continental army's victory in the American Revolution was like the
Blue team's victory in Capture the Flag . . .

. . . because the Continental army defeated a much larger, more experienced
opponent—the British army—just like the Blue team defeated a much more
experienced opponent, the Red team.

Chapter 7 Assessment

Mastering the Content

Fill in the circle next to the best answer.

1. Which of these was a weakness of the Continental army at the start of the war?
   - ○ A. supply shortages
   - ○ B. weak commander
   - ○ C. unfamiliar territory
   - ○ D. long travel distances

2. At the start of the war, what was a weakness of the British troops?
   - ○ A. poor leadership
   - ○ B. understaffed army
   - ○ C. insufficient supplies
   - ○ D. poorly trained soldiers

3. Why did African Americans join the Continental army?
   - ○ A. They had excellent military skills.
   - ○ B. They were generously paid to join the army.
   - ○ C. They blamed Great Britain for their enslavement.
   - ○ D. They hoped independence would lead to an end of slavery.

4. Which of these was an effect of African Americans helping the cause of independence?
   - ○ A. Slavery was abolished throughout the colonies.
   - ○ B. Several colonies began to take steps to end slavery.
   - ○ C. African Americans who fought were given their freedom.
   - ○ D. African Americans were respected and their brave acts rewarded.

5. What caused the American defeat in Brooklyn, New York, in August 1776?
   - ○ A. weak leadership
   - ○ B. unmotivated troops
   - ○ C. undisciplined enemy
   - ○ D. inexperienced soldiers

6. Read the quotation, which General Washington read to his soldiers.

   > "The summer soldier and the sunshine patriot will, in this crisis, shrink from the service of their country."

   Which word describes the "summer soldier and sunshine patriot"?
   - ○ A. traitors
   - ○ B. fighters
   - ○ C. quitters
   - ○ D. optimists

7. Which statement describes Washington's military strategy after 1776?
   - ○ A. to avoid battles with the British
   - ○ B. to defeat the British in one large battle
   - ○ C. to fight a defensive war and tire the British out
   - ○ D. to prevent food and supplies from reaching the British

8. Which of these was an effect of the American victory at Saratoga?
   - ○ A. British troops gained confidence.
   - ○ B. General Burgoyne resigned his post.
   - ○ C. Great Britain withdrew from Canada.
   - ○ D. European countries came to the aid of America.

9. Which of these nations became an American ally after the victory at Saratoga?

○ A. France
○ B. Canada
○ C. Mexico
○ D. Germany

10. Why did many of the British people not support the war?

○ A. The king was unpopular.
○ B. They planned to move to America.
○ C. The cost to taxpayers was too high.
○ D. They wanted the Americans to have their independence.

11. What was the result of the American victories at Trenton and Princeton?

○ A. The Hessians joined the American side.
○ B. It showed that the Americans could defeat the British.
○ C. It proved that General Washington was wrong about his soldiers.
○ D. The British were forced to abandon New York and New Jersey.

12. Which of these was a clear disadvantage for General Burgoyne in Albany, New York?

○ A. unfamiliar territory
○ B. not enough soldiers
○ C. insufficient supplies
○ D. poor communication

13. Which group prevented a British victory in the South?

○ A. Loyalists
○ B. mercenaries
○ C. French soldiers
○ D. guerrilla troops

14. Which of these describes the progress of the war?

○ A. The British won every battle until the final one.
○ B. The British soldiers lost most of the battles against the disciplined American soldiers.
○ C. At the beginning, the Americans were outmatched, but their skills and tactics improved.
○ D. The Americans outnumbered the British, finally defeating them at the Battle of Yorktown.

15. How did the American Revolution impact other parts of the world?

○ A. It led to Great Britain giving up its other colonies.
○ B. It made other nations fearful of American strength.
○ C. It encouraged other nations to fight for their independence.
○ D. It made citizens of other nations fearful of a fight for independence.

16. In addition to independence, what did the Treaty of Paris give to the Americans?

○ A. British land in Canada
○ B. the right to punish the Loyalists
○ C. land east of the Mississippi River
○ D. the return of taxes paid to Great Britain

Applying Social Studies Skills

Use the map and your knowledge of history to answer these questions.

The Battle of Yorktown

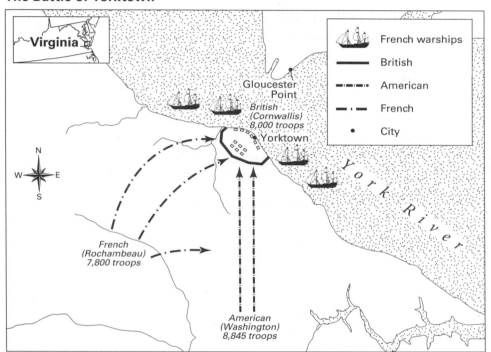

17. In which colonial region did the Battle of Yorktown take place?

18. What prevented the British from being rescued by the British navy?

19. How were the British defeated at the Battle of Yorktown?

Exploring the Essential Question

How was the Continental army able to win the war for independence from Great Britain?

Follow the directions to complete the item below.

20. Suppose you were an American soldier in the American Revolution. You are asked to write a short essay about the person who most inspired the Continental army to win the war. You have chosen George Washington. The title of your essay is "How General Washington Inspired the Continental Army to Win the War." Your essay should have three paragraphs:

- The first paragraph describes characteristics of General Washington that prepared him for his role as commander of the Continental army.

- The second paragraph supports your choice by citing two events at which Washington provided inspiration.

- The third paragraph identifies how these actions or events led to an American victory.

Make sure to convey your ideas clearly, using standard English.

Unit 2 Timeline Challenge Cards

French and Indian War
1754–1763

This war between France and Great Britain results in a victory for Great Britain and a vastly expanded American empire.

Colonial Taxation
1763–1767

British Parliament passes a series of taxes on the colonies, resulting in protests from many colonists.

Boston Massacre
1770

Five Bostonians are killed during a brawl between colonists and British soldiers. The incident causes an outcry of injustice throughout the colonies.

Intolerable Acts
1774

British Parliament passes the Intolerable Acts to punish the colonists for their support of the Boston Tea Party.

First Continental Congress
1774

Fifty leaders from the colonies meet to devise peaceful solutions to the conflicts with Great Britain.

Battles of Lexington and Concord
1775

Lexington and Concord become the first sites where the British army and colonial militias battle over control of the colonies. The clashes mark the start of the war for independence from Great Britain.

Battle of Bunker Hill
1775

British troops invade colonial fortifications overlooking Boston in the Battle of Bunker Hill.

Common Sense
1776

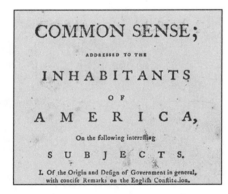

COMMON SENSE;

ADDRESSED TO THE

INHABITANTS

OF

AMERICA,

On the following interesting

SUBJECTS.

I. Of the Origin and Design of Government in general, with concise Remarks on the English Constitution.

Thomas Paine writes *Common Sense*, which persuades many colonists to support the idea that the colonies should be independent from Great Britain.

Declaration of Independence
1776

The Declaration of Independence is approved by the Second Continental Congress and declares to the world that the British colonies are now a free and independent nation.

Battles of Trenton and Princeton
Dec. 1776–Jan. 1777

American victories in these battles reenergize the Continental army after it suffers many defeats in previous battles with the British army.

Battle of Yorktown
1781

The British army surrenders at Yorktown, Virginia, after being trapped by American and French forces.

Treaty of Paris
1783

The Treaty of Paris is signed, formally ending the war fought between Great Britain and the United States during the American Revolution.

Experiencing the Weaknesses of the Articles of Confederation

Articles of Confederation	Classroom Experience
Congress was composed of 13 states.	The class was divided into 13 groups.
Each state had one vote in Congress.	Each group of students had one vote.
Congress dealt with many problems, such as how to develop the western lands acquired by the United States in the Treaty of Paris.	Students tried to choose a radio station to listen to.
Congress failed to resolve disputes between states over taxes and boundaries.	The class failed to choose a station to listen to.
Many citizens were concerned that the government was too weak.	Some students became dissatisfied and frustrated.

Debating at the Convention

Proposals for How States Will Be Represented in the New Government

Proposal A
The number of representatives a state sends to Congress will depend on the size of the state's population.

Proposal B
Each state will have an equal number of representatives in Congress, regardless of the state's size.

Proposal C
The number of representatives a state sends to Congress will depend partially on the wealth of the citizens of the state.

Procedure for Discussing the Proposals

Follow these steps to discuss how states should be represented in the new government.

Step 1: One state delegation nominates one of the proposals above.

Step 2: The nomination is seconded by another state.

Step 3: The nomination is discussed and debated for three to five minutes.

Step 4: The nominated proposal is voted upon. To pass, the nomination must be approved by a majority of the states. A majority means that a proposal receives more than half of the votes.

Step 5: If the proposal does not pass, repeat the process with a new nomination.

Role Cards for Constitutional Convention Delegates

John Langdon   New Hampshire (small state)

Personal Background and Character You were an early supporter of the American Revolution. You represented your state in the Continental Congress and fought in the war. Since that time, you have held important political positions in your state, including speaker of the New Hampshire assembly and governor of New Hampshire. You are optimistic, cheerful, and an active speaker in the debates at the Constitutional Convention.

Views You agree with Proposal B. You believe that all states should have an equal vote in Congress. You think Congress should have one house. (**Note:** You will receive 10 extra credit points if the proposal you support at the convention is chosen.)

Points to Raise During the Convention The larger states could "gang up" on the smaller states.

Sign the Constitution? Yes.

Nicolas Gilman   New Hampshire (small state)

Personal Background and Character Growing up in New Hampshire, you attended local schools and worked in your father's general store. During the war for independence, you became a captain in the Continental army and served through the war. After the war, your main interest became politics. You were a delegate in the Continental Congress from 1786 to 1788. Because you are one of the more inexperienced delegates, you pay careful attention to the discussions during the Constitutional Convention.

Views You agree with Proposal B. You believe that all states should have an equal vote in Congress. You think Congress should have one house. (**Note:** You will receive 10 extra credit points if the proposal you support at the convention is chosen.)

Points to Raise During the Convention The larger states could "gang up" on the smaller states.

Sign the Constitution? Yes.

Elbridge Gerry

Massachusetts (large state)

Personal Background and Character You were born to a wealthy family and joined the family merchant and shipping business after graduating from Harvard College. You served in the colonial legislature and became one of the first Patriots. In 1776, you became a delegate to the Continental Congress. You are known for being somewhat nervous and very serious, without much of a sense of humor.

Views You agree with Proposal A. You believe that states should be represented in Congress based on their population. You think Congress should have two houses. (**Note:** You will receive 10 extra credit points if the proposal you support at the convention is chosen.)

Points to Raise During the Convention A strong national government is best, but we must make sure the rights of the people are protected. The American people must have a direct connection to their government.

Sign the Constitution? No. You believe that the new government is worse than the old one. You want a bill of rights and other changes to better protect people's rights and liberties.

Rufus King

Massachusetts (large state)

Personal Background and Character You grew up the son of a farmer and merchant. After attending Harvard College, you served briefly in the war for independence and then became a lawyer. You are very active in politics, serving as a member of the Massachusetts legislature and the Continental Congress. You are known as a brilliant speaker and an opponent of slavery. When you first arrived at the convention, you did not want to see the Articles of Confederation greatly altered.

Views You agree with Proposal C. You believe that states should be represented in Congress based on how much property their citizens have. You think Congress should have two houses. (**Note:** You will receive 10 extra credit points if the proposal you support at the convention is chosen.)

Points to Raise During the Convention The American people should have a direct connection to their government. You become very frustrated with the small states' unwillingness to give up their proposal. You take the position that if the small states won't budge on the issue of representation, then neither will you.

Sign the Constitution? Yes.

Roger Sherman   Connecticut (medium state)

Personal Background You grew up on a farm and learned the shoemaking trade as a young man. Even though you were not trained in law, you became a lawyer and a judge and eventually a leader in your community. You served in the Continental Congress, where you were appointed to the committees that drafted the Declaration of Independence and the Articles of Confederation. You are a respected leader who is known for your careful reasoning and skill in debate as well as your willingness to compromise.

Views You agree with Proposals A and B. You want to combine them into one proposal to create a Congress with two houses. In the lower house, states would be represented by population. In the upper house, each state would have equal representation. (**Note:** You will receive 10 extra credit points if the proposal you support at the convention is chosen.)

Points to Raise During the Convention You will present your compromise proposal (see "Views" above) during the debate, but not at first. You realize you do not have enough support for your proposal at the beginning of the convention. So you wait until the convention is deadlocked (and must compromise) and then nominate your proposal.

Sign the Constitution? Yes.

Oliver Ellsworth   Connecticut (medium state)

Personal Background and Character After graduating from the College of New Jersey, you became a successful lawyer. You are an active participant at the Constitutional Convention. You proposed that official documents refer to the government as the "United States." Your proposal was accepted by the convention. Tall and dignified, you sometimes show a sharp temper.

Views You agree with Proposal B. You believe that all states should have an equal vote in Congress. You think Congress should have one house, but you are willing to compromise on this. (**Note:** You will receive 10 extra credit points if the proposal you support at the convention is chosen.)

Points to Raise During the Convention The larger states could "gang up" on the smaller states. The few must be protected from destruction by the many.

Sign the Constitution? No. You leave the convention before the signing, but you will support ratification.

Alexander Hamilton
New York (large state)

Personal Background and Character You were born in the British West Indies. As a youth, you showed great intelligence and talent. After your mother died, people on your island raised money to send you to school in New York. During the American Revolution, you wrote several pamphlets to support the Patriot cause. When war broke out, you became an army officer and quickly rose to become an assistant to General George Washington. After the war, you became a lawyer, were elected to the Continental Congress, and later served in the state legislature. You are charming, passionate, and ambitious. You are a leading supporter of creating a strong central government.

Views You agree with Proposal A. You believe that states should be represented in Congress based on their population. You think Congress should have two houses. (**Note:** You will receive 10 extra credit points if the proposal you support at the convention is chosen.)

Points to Raise During the Convention The American people should have a direct connection to their government. Choosing representatives in this way will ensure that more voices will be represented in the government, not just one voice from each state. Your fellow delegates from New York have a different opinion and you constantly disagree with them.

Sign the Constitution? Yes.

Robert Yates
New York (large state)

Personal Background and Character As a young man, you studied law in New York City and then became a lawyer in Albany, New York. During the American Revolution, you helped draft the first constitution for the state of New York. You served on New York's state supreme court, where some people criticized you for your fair treatment of Loyalists. Many people think you are arrogant and snobbish.

Views You agree with Proposal B. You believe that all states must have an equal vote in Congress. You think Congress should have one house. (**Note:** You will receive 10 extra credit points if the proposal you support at the convention is chosen.)

Points to Raise During the Convention If Congress becomes too strong, it may abuse states' rights. The convention is simply supposed to improve the Articles of Confederation. You do not believe that the convention has the authority to create a new government. You constantly disagree with your fellow delegate, Alexander Hamilton.

Sign the Constitution? No. You leave the convention when it becomes clear that it will form a powerful new national government instead of simply revising the Articles of Confederation.

William Paterson   New Jersey (small state)

Personal Background and Character When you were two years old, your family moved from Ireland to New Jersey, where your father became a prosperous merchant. After graduating from the College of New Jersey, you studied law. You were a lawyer by the time the American Revolution began. You were a leading Patriot during the war. In 1776, you became New Jersey's attorney general. You are known to be hardworking, serious, and formal.

Views You agree with Proposal B. You firmly believe that all states must have an equal vote in Congress. You think Congress should have one house. (**Note:** You will receive 10 extra credit points if the proposal you support at the convention is chosen.)

Points to Raise During the Convention If Congress becomes too strong, it may abuse states' rights. A strong national government is important, but if too much power is given to Congress, small states could be swallowed up by the larger states. Small states could lose their voice in government.

Sign the Constitution? Yes.

David Brearley   New Jersey (small state)

Personal Background and Character You were born in New Jersey and come from an old English family. You chose law as a career. A strong supporter of the American Revolution, you were arrested by the British for treason and freed by a group of Patriots. You served as an officer during the war. In 1779, you were elected chief justice of the New Jersey Supreme Court. As a delegate to the Constitutional Convention, you faithfully attend the sessions.

Views You agree with Proposal B. You firmly believe that all states must have an equal vote in Congress. You think Congress should have one house. (**Note:** You will receive 10 extra credit points if the proposal you support at the convention is chosen.)

Points to Raise During the Convention The larger states could "gang up" on the smaller states. You are frustrated during the debate. You sarcastically announce to the delegates that maybe the states should be thrown out and the country should be cut up into 13 equal pieces.

Sign the Constitution? Yes.

Benjamin Franklin   Pennsylvania (large state)

Personal Background and Character You are one of the most respected men in the United States. You have achieved fame as a scientist, inventor, diplomat, and politician. Your accomplishments include helping draft the Declaration of Independence. As a representative to France, you helped convince the French government to support the American Revolution. Despite your age and poor health, you faithfully attend sessions of the convention. You arrived willing to support any proposal that would create a more effective government. Your wisdom, humor, and calming influence help the delegates resolve bitter disagreements.

Views You agree with Proposal A. You believe that states should be represented in Congress based on their population. You think Congress should have one house. (**Note:** You will receive 10 extra credit points if the proposal you support at the convention is chosen.)

Points to Raise During the Convention Delegates must not argue with each other, but remain calm and keep their tempers. Letting the convention fall apart will only please the nation's enemies. Delegates must work hard to create a strong, unified government.

Sign the Constitution? Yes. On the last day of the convention, you rise and ask every delegate to sign the Constitution in a show of unity. You confess that you do not agree with every part of it. But you believe it is as close to perfect as possible and that this new government will surprise the nation's enemies, who have been waiting for the new nation to fail.

Gouverneur Morris   Pennsylvania (large state)

Personal Background and Character You were well educated as a youth and eventually became a lawyer. When the American Revolution began, many of your friends were Loyalists. Although you worried about mob rule, you sided with the Patriots. You helped write New York's state constitution and later served in the state legislature and Continental Congress. You moved to Pennsylvania in 1779, where you now practice law. A colorful and forceful speaker, you are one of the most active speakers at the Constitutional Convention.

Views You agree with Proposals A, B, and C. You think Congress should have two houses. In the first house, all states should have an equal vote. In the second house, representation should be based on the amount of property and wealth a state has, as well as the size of its population. (**Note:** You will receive 10 extra credit points if the proposal you support at the convention is chosen.)

Points to Raise During the Convention The wealthy should have their own house in Congress so that they will not try to control the other parts of the government.

Sign the Constitution? Yes.

James Wilson
Pennsylvania (large state)

Personal Background and Character As a young man, you studied law and became involved in the American Revolution by writing a popular pamphlet on the British Parliament. You were one of the signers of the Declaration of Independence. During the war, you were a cautious Patriot who associated with the wealthy and powerful. You even defended the interests of Loyalists. You have been elected to Congress twice. You are respected for your honesty and are very influential at the Constitutional Convention, where you are one of the most active speakers.

Views You agree with Proposal A. You strongly believe that states must be represented in Congress on the basis of their populations. You think Congress should have two houses. (**Note:** You will receive 10 extra credit points if the proposal you support at the convention is chosen.)

Points to Raise During the Convention Why should a smaller state, with fewer people, have more power than a larger state? If the small states will not agree on this plan, then Pennsylvania—and you are sure others—will not agree on any plan.

Sign the Constitution? Yes.

John Dickinson
Delaware (small state)

Personal Background and Character You grew up in a prosperous family and became a well-known lawyer. When the American Revolution began, you looked for peaceful ways to resolve the conflict. At the Second Continental Congress, you refused to sign the Declaration of Independence. You served as president of the Delaware Supreme Executive Council and as president of Pennsylvania. You are Delaware's delegate to the Constitutional Convention. You are a nervous and cautious man.

Views You agree with Proposals B and C. You propose that Congress should have two houses. In the first house, all states should have an equal vote. In the second house, representation should be based on the amount of taxes a state pays to the national government. (**Note:** You will receive 10 extra credit points if the proposal you support at the convention is chosen.)

Points to Raise During the Convention You are willing to compromise. You are in favor of a stronger central government, but refuse to vote for Proposal A only. Small states must have an equal voice in the national government.

Sign the Constitution? Yes.

Gunning Bedford Jr.
Delaware (small state)

Personal Background and Character You grew up in a prominent family and were educated to become a lawyer. During the war for independence, you served in the Continental army. Later you served in the state legislature, on the state council, and in the Continental Congress. In 1784, you became attorney general of Delaware. Forceful and hot-tempered, you are a very active member of the Constitutional Convention.

Views You agree with Proposal B. You strongly believe that all states must have an equal vote in Congress. You think Congress should have one house, but are willing to compromise on this point. (**Note:** You will receive 10 extra credit points if the proposal you support at the convention is chosen.)

Points to Raise During the Convention If the national government becomes too strong, it may abuse states' rights. After listening to the arguments of delegates from larger states, you become angry and say, "They insist they will never hurt or injure the [smaller] states. I do not, gentlemen, trust you!" If the national government does not protect the smaller states, then the smaller states might have to make partnerships with foreign countries.

Sign the Constitution? Yes.

Luther Martin
Maryland (medium state)

Personal Background and Character After graduating from college in New Jersey, you moved to Maryland, where you taught school and studied law. An early supporter of independence, you became attorney general of Maryland and often brought charges against Loyalists. You fought with the Baltimore Light Dragoons during the war for independence. Your law practice became one of the largest and most successful in the country. At the Constitutional Convention, you are an emotional speaker for states' rights and often speak for hours at a time.

Views You agree with Proposal B. You believe that all states must have an equal vote in Congress. You think Congress should have one house. (**Note:** You will receive 10 extra credit points if the proposal you support at the convention is chosen.)

Points to Raise During the Convention If the national government becomes too strong, it may abuse states' rights. The best kind of government gives power to state governments, not directly to the people. Personal interests are being put ahead of the common good at this convention.

Sign the Constitution? No. You walk out of the convention because you believe that the Constitution gives Congress too much power compared to the states and that the system of representation in Congress is unfair.

James McHenry   Maryland (medium state)

Personal Background and Character You came from Ireland to America as a young man, started a business, and studied medicine in school. During the war for independence, you served as a surgeon and were captured by the British. After your release, you served as secretary to General Washington. After the war, you were elected to both the Maryland Senate and the Continental Congress. Quiet and sensible, you keep a private journal during the Constitutional Convention that will prove to be useful to historians in future years.

Views You agree with Proposal B. You believe that all states must have an equal vote in Congress. You think Congress should have one house. (**Note:** You will receive 10 extra credit points if the proposal you support at the convention is chosen.)

Points to Raise During the Convention A stronger government is necessary, but the larger states could "gang up" on the smaller states.

Sign the Constitution? Yes.

James Madison   Virginia (large state)

Personal Background and Character As a youth, you received an excellent education from private tutors and in private schools. After college, you became a Patriot and were active in politics. You helped draft Virginia's constitution, served in the House of Delegates, and represented Virginia in the Continental Congress. You wrote numerous articles about the problems with the Articles of Confederation, and you were one of the main voices to call for the Constitutional Convention. Although you are not a great speaker, you speak dozens of times at the convention. At the convention, you work tirelessly for a strong central government. You are the single most influential delegate. Your detailed journal is the best record of the convention.

Views You agree with Proposal A. You strongly believe that states should be represented in Congress on the basis of their population. You think Congress should have two houses. (**Note:** You will receive 10 extra credit points if the proposal you support at the convention is chosen.)

Points to Raise During the Convention The American people should have a direct connection to their government. Choosing representatives in this way will ensure that more voices will be represented in the government, not just one voice from each state.

Sign the Constitution? Yes.

George Mason

Virginia (large state)

Personal Background and Character At the age of ten, you went to live with your uncle after your father died. Your education was shaped by your uncle's huge library, one-third of which concerned the law. Later you became one of the richest planters in Virginia and an important figure in your community. You served as a judge and in Virginia's House of Burgesses and helped to form a new government in Virginia during the American Revolution. At the Constitutional Convention, you speak frequently. Your approach is cool, reasonable, and free from personal attacks.

Views You agree with Proposal A. You believe that states should be represented in Congress based on their population. You think Congress should have two houses. (**Note:** You will receive 10 extra credit points if the proposal you support at the convention is chosen.)

Points to Raise During the Convention A strong national government is necessary, but individual rights must be protected. It is important to make sure the government is truly representing the people.

Sign the Constitution? No. You want the Constitution to include a bill of rights, and you fear that the new government either will become a monarchy or be controlled by the wealthy few.

Hugh Williamson

North Carolina (medium state)

Personal Background and Character You are a man of many talents, especially in science and medicine. Benjamin Franklin, a fellow scientist, is one of your best friends. Before the war, you wrote a pamphlet encouraging English support of the colonies' complaints against Great Britain. Later, you were elected to the state legislature and the Continental Congress. You are a hard worker at the Constitutional Convention and an enthusiastic and skilled public speaker during the debates.

Views You agree with Proposals A and C. You believe that states should be represented in Congress based on their population and wealth. You think Congress should have one house. (**Note:** You will receive 10 extra credit points if the proposal you support at the convention is chosen.)

Points to Raise During the Convention Even though North Carolina is smaller than other states, there is good reason to support Proposal A. There is a lot of unsettled land in the western part of the state and one day, when more settlers arrive, it will have a larger population. If we support Proposal A now, someday North Carolina will have more power in the government.

Sign the Constitution? Yes.

William Blount   North Carolina (medium state)

Personal Background and Character You received a good education as a youth. During the war for independence, you joined the North Carolina militia as a paymaster. After the war, you became active in politics and served in the North Carolina legislature and as a delegate to the Continental Congress. You are absent from the Constitutional Convention for more than a month while you attend the Continental Congress. As the convention goes on, you are cautious in your support of the Constitution. A fellow delegate describes you as "plain, honest, and sincere."

Views You agree with Proposal A. You believe that states should be represented in Congress based on their population. You think Congress should have one house. (**Note:** You will receive 10 extra credit points if the proposal you support at the convention is chosen.)

Points to Raise During the Convention Even though North Carolina is smaller than other states, there is good reason to support Proposal A. There is a lot of unsettled land in the western part of the state and one day, when more settlers arrive, it will have a larger population. If we support Proposal A now, someday North Carolina will have more power in the government.

Sign the Constitution? Yes.

John Rutledge   South Carolina (medium state)

Personal Background and Character You studied law in London and then returned to South Carolina, where you practiced law. A moderate Patriot, you tried to avoid a complete break with Great Britain in the years leading up to the American Revolution. You have served in the state legislature, the Continental Congress, as governor, and as a judge. At the Constitutional Convention, you speak often and effectively, arguing for the interests of southern states. Always courteous, you are careful not to offend others.

Views You agree with Proposals A and C. You believe that states should be represented in Congress based on their wealth and population. You think Congress should have two houses. (**Note:** You will receive 10 extra credit points if the proposal you support at the convention is chosen.)

Points to Raise During the Convention Even though South Carolina is a smaller state, there is good reason to support Proposal A. There is a lot of unsettled land in the western part of the state and one day, when more settlers arrive, it will have a larger population. If we support Proposal A now, someday South Carolina will have more power in the government.

Sign the Constitution? Yes.

Charles Cotesworth Pinckney   South Carolina (medium state)

Personal Background and Character You graduated from Oxford University in England and then studied law and science. After returning to South Carolina, you practiced law and soon joined the Patriot cause and helped plan a temporary new government for South Carolina. During the war for independence, you rose to the rank of colonel and also served in the state legislature. You spent nearly two years as a prisoner of the British. You are a leading participant at the Constitutional Convention, speaking out for a powerful national government.

Views You agree with Proposals A and B. You believe that Congress should have two houses. In the lower house, states should be represented based on their population. In the upper house, each state should have one vote. (**Note:** You will receive 10 extra credit points if the proposal you support at the convention is chosen.)

Points to Raise During the Convention Even though South Carolina is a smaller state, there is good reason to support Proposal A. There is a lot of unsettled land in the western part of the state and one day, when more settlers arrive, it will have a larger population. If we support Proposal A now, someday South Carolina will have more power in the government.

Sign the Constitution? Yes.

Abraham Baldwin   Georgia (small state)

Personal Background and Character You grew up in Connecticut. Your father, a blacksmith, went into debt to educate you and his other children. Later, you graduated from Yale University and became a minister. During the war for independence, you served as a chaplain in the Continental army. Then you studied law and moved to Georgia, where you became a lawyer, served in the state assembly, and represented Georgia in the Continental Congress. Other delegates find you likeable and reasonable.

Views You agree with Proposal C. You believe that states should be represented in Congress based on their property and wealth, but you are open to the argument that all states should have an equal vote. You think Congress should have one house. (**Note:** You will receive 10 extra credit points if the proposal you support at the convention is chosen.)

Points to Raise During the Convention Representation in the Senate based on the amount of property owned is the best proposal. It is better, however, to compromise so that this convention is able to stay together.

Sign the Constitution? Yes.

William Few   Georgia (small state)

Personal Background and Character You grew up in a poor family and received little schooling. One of your brothers was hanged as a result of a fight between frontier settlers and the royal governor, and the family farm was destroyed. Later, you became a lawyer. When the war for independence began, you were an enthusiastic Patriot and served as a lieutenant colonel in the Continental army. After the war, you served in the state assembly and the Continental Congress. You miss a good part of the Constitutional Convention while you are busy in Congress. You are one of the only "self-made" men at the convention.

Views You agree with Proposal A. You believe that states should be represented in Congress based on their population. You think Congress should have one house. (**Note:** You will receive 10 extra credit points if the proposal you support at the convention is chosen.)

Points to Raise During the Convention Even though Georgia is a small state, there is good reason to support Proposal A. There is a lot of unsettled land in the western part of the state and one day, when more settlers arrive, it will have a larger population. If we support Proposal A now, someday Georgia will have more power in the government.

Sign the Constitution? Yes.

John Lansing Jr.   New York (large state)

Personal Background and Character You own a law practice and a large estate, both of which have made you quite wealthy. As a politician, you have served several terms in the New York assembly and are currently the mayor of Albany. You are suspicious that this convention may go beyond simply improving the Articles of Confederation and might try to create a more powerful central government, which could reduce New York's power.

Views You agree with Proposal B. You believe that all states must have an equal vote in Congress. You think Congress should have one house. (**Note:** You will receive 10 extra credit points if the proposal you support at the convention is chosen.)

Points to Raise During the Convention If Congress becomes too strong, it may abuse states' rights. The convention is simply supposed to improve the Articles of Confederation. You do not believe that the convention has the authority to create a new government. You constantly disagree with your fellow delegate, Alexander Hamilton.

Sign the Constitution? No. You quit the convention when it becomes clear that it will form a powerful new national government instead of simply revising the Articles of Confederation.

Nathaniel Gorham   Massachusetts (large state)

Personal Background and Character You received little formal education as a youth and worked as an apprentice to a merchant before starting your own business. During the war for independence, British troops destroyed much of your property, but you regained your wealth by raiding shipping as a privateer. You have served in the state legislature, the Continental Congress, and the Governor's Council. You are now a judge. You attend every session of the Constitutional Convention. You are easygoing and friendly and often speak out in debates.

Views You agree with Proposal A. You believe that states should be represented in Congress based on their population. You think Congress should have two houses. (**Note:** You will receive 10 extra credit points if the proposal you support at the convention is chosen.)

Points to Raise During the Convention You would rather see the convention fall apart before compromising with the smaller states.

Sign the Constitution? Yes.

Edmund Randolph   Virginia (large state)

Personal Background and Character You were educated as a lawyer. When the American Revolution began, your father, a Loyalist, moved to England. You then lived with your uncle, Peyton Randolph, an important figure in Virginia politics. You became an aide to General Washington. At age 23, you helped Virginia adopt its first state constitution. Continuing your political career, you served as mayor of Williamsburg, as Virginia's attorney general, as a delegate to the Continental Congress, and as governor of Virginia.

Views You agree with Proposal A. You believe that states should be represented in Congress based on their population. You think Congress should have two houses. (**Note:** You will receive 10 extra credit points if the proposal you support at the convention is chosen.)

Points to Raise During the Convention Although you favor lessening the power of the states and strengthening the national government, you worry about Congress becoming too powerful.

Sign the Constitution? No. You are opposed to a one-person executive, which you fear could lead to a monarchy.

William Samuel Johnson   Connecticut (medium state)

Personal Background and Character You are well educated and graduated from Yale University. With no formal training in law, you became a prosperous lawyer and later a judge of Connecticut's highest court. When the American Revolution began, you found it hard to choose sides. At first, you worked to end the dispute with Great Britain peacefully, and you refused to participate in the First Continental Congress. After the war, however, you became a popular and respected delegate in the Continental Congress. You are cautious and dislike controversy.

Views You agree with Proposal B. You believe all states should have an equal vote in Congress. You think Congress should have one house, but you are willing to compromise on this. (**Note:** You will receive 10 extra credit points if the proposal you support at the convention is chosen.)

Points to Raise During the Convention The larger states could "gang up" on the smaller states.

Sign the Constitution? Yes.

Jonathan Dayton   New Jersey (small state)

Personal Background and Character You received a good education and graduated from the College of New Jersey in 1776. You immediately joined the Continental army, where you became a captain by the age of 19 and were imprisoned for a time by the British. After the war, you returned home, studied law, established a law practice, and served in the state assembly. At the Constitutional Convention, you faithfully attend sessions and take part in debates. You are seen as honest, but are sometimes quick-tempered.

Views You agree with Proposal B. You firmly believe that all states must have an equal vote in Congress. You think Congress should have one house. (**Note:** You will receive 10 extra credit points if the proposal you support at the convention is chosen.)

Points to Raise During the Convention The larger states could "gang up" on the smaller states. You believe that scare tactics suggesting that the convention will fail if the small states do not change their position will not work.

Sign the Constitution? Yes.

George Read

Delaware (small state)

Personal Background and Character You became a lawyer and, in 1765, began a career in the colonial legislature that lasted more than a decade. As a delegate to the Continental Congress, you supported colonial rights, but you were the only signer of the Declaration of Independence to vote against independence. You served on the state legislative council and presided over the Delaware constitutional convention. After a narrow escape from the British during the war, you served as president of Delaware and are now a judge. At the Constitutional Convention, you attend sessions faithfully and defend the rights of small states.

Views You agree with Proposal B. You strongly believe that all states must have an equal vote in Congress. You think Congress should have one house. (**Note:** You will receive 10 extra credit points if the proposal you support at the convention is chosen.)

Points to Raise During the Convention The larger states could "gang up" on the smaller states.

Sign the Constitution? Yes.

Daniel Carroll

Maryland (medium state)

Personal Background and Character You were born to a wealthy Catholic family and went to school in Europe. After returning to America, you were a reluctant supporter of the American Revolution. As a wealthy planter, you took little part in public life until 1781, when you were elected to the Continental Congress, where you signed the Articles of Confederation. You have served in the Maryland Senate and you are a good friend of George Washington. You faithfully attend sessions of the Constitutional Convention and give about 20 speeches during the debates.

Views You agree with Proposal A. You believe that states should be represented in Congress based on their population. You think Congress should have two houses. (**Note:** You will receive 10 extra credit points if the proposal you support at the convention is chosen.)

Points to Raise During the Convention The American people should have a direct connection to their government. Choosing representatives in this way will ensure that more voices will be represented in the government, not just one voice from each state.

Sign the Constitution? Yes.

Delegate Masks

John Langdon

Nicolas Gilman

Elbridge Gerry

Rufus King

Roger Sherman

Oliver Ellsworth

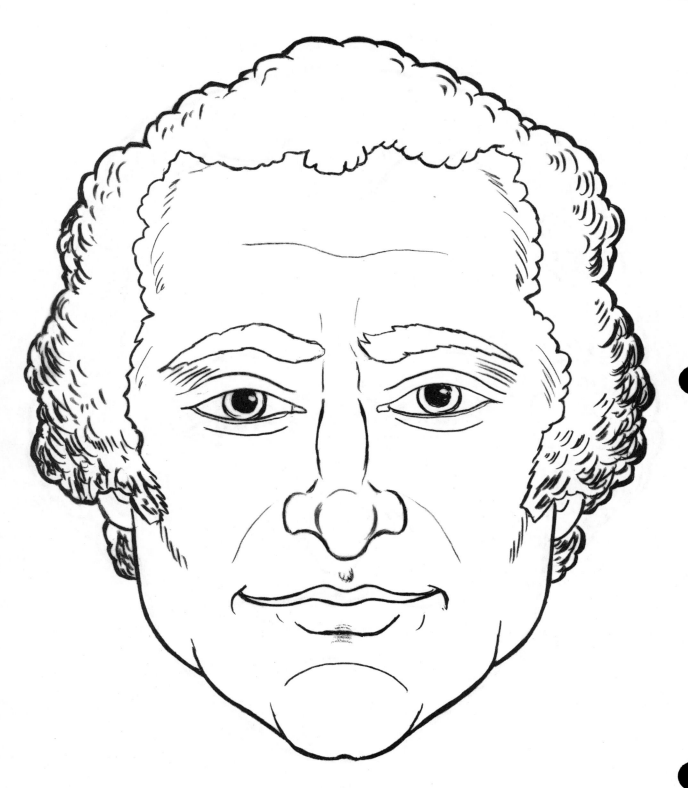

Alexander Hamilton

Robert Yates

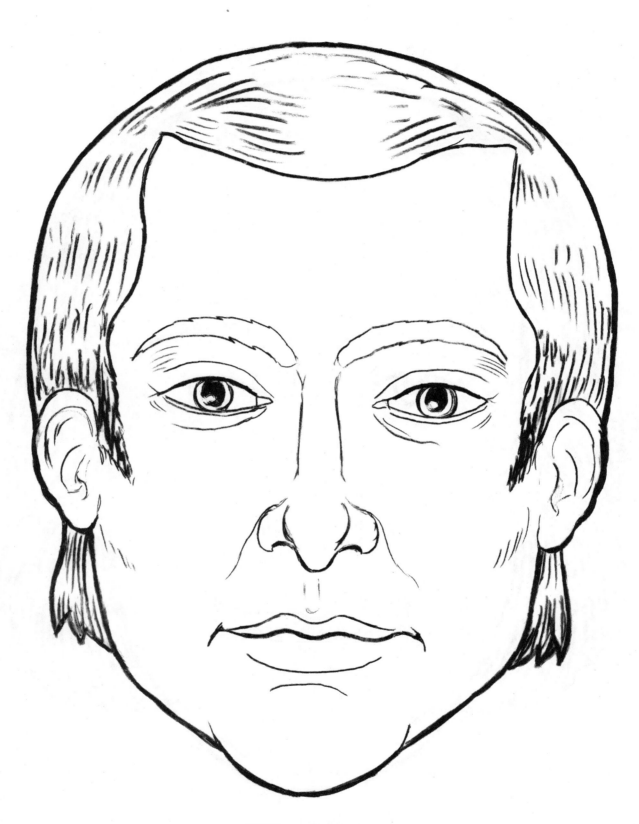

William Paterson

David Brearley

Benjamin Franklin

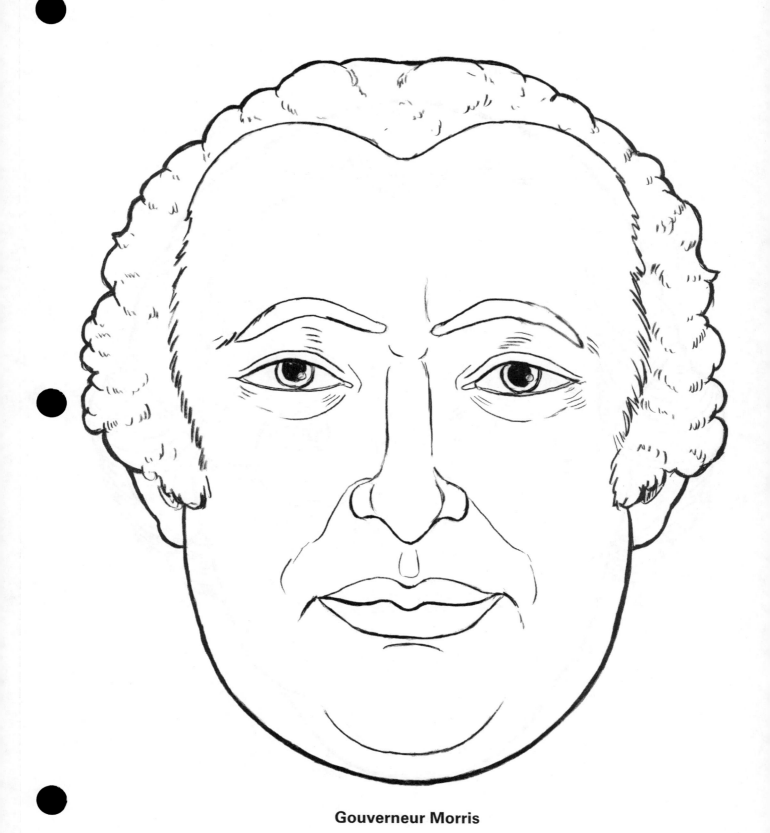

Gouverneur Morris

James Wilson

John Dickinson

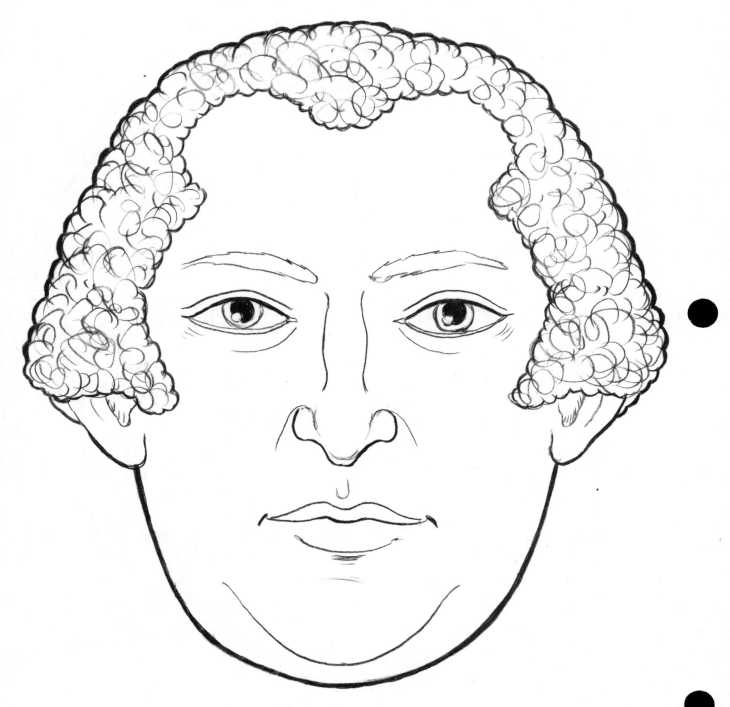

Gunning Bedford Jr.

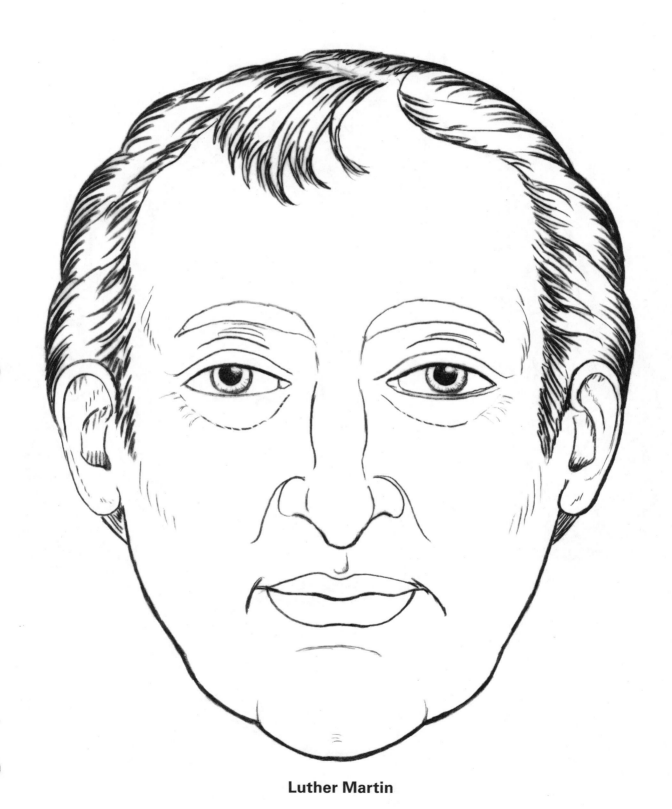

Luther Martin

James McHenry

James Madison

George Mason

Hugh Williamson

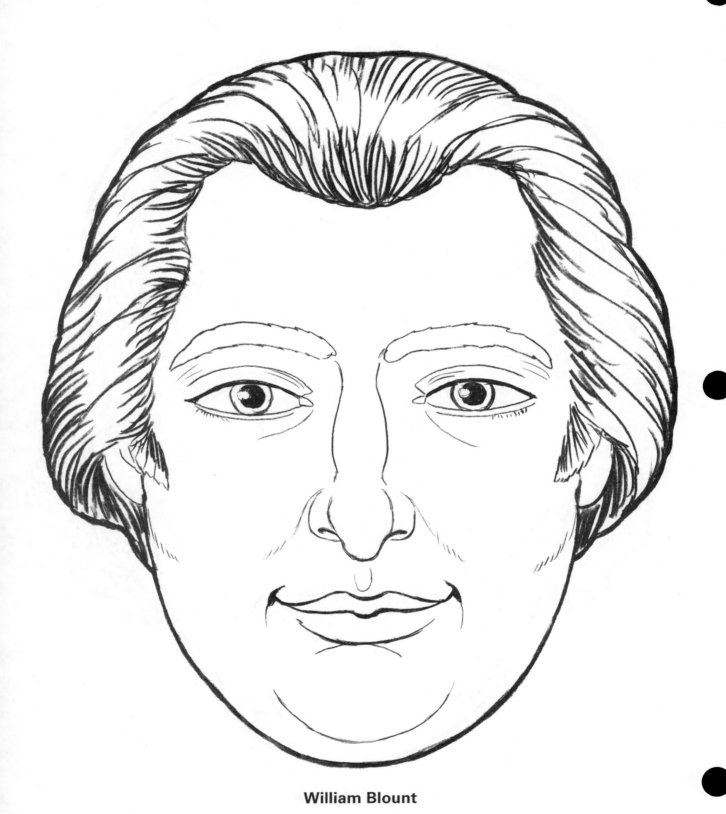

William Blount

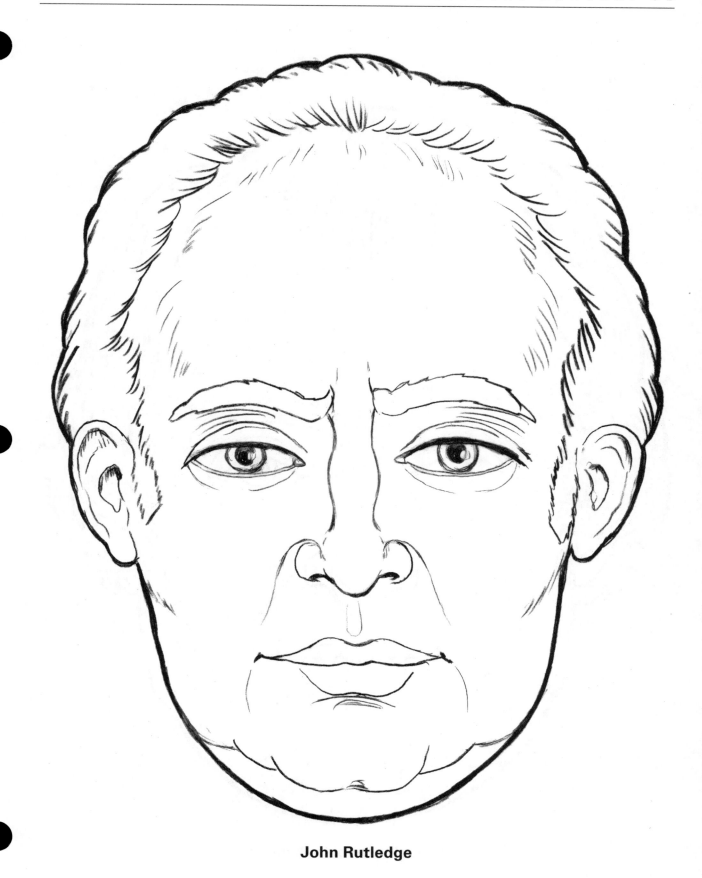

John Rutledge

Charles Cotesworth Pinckney

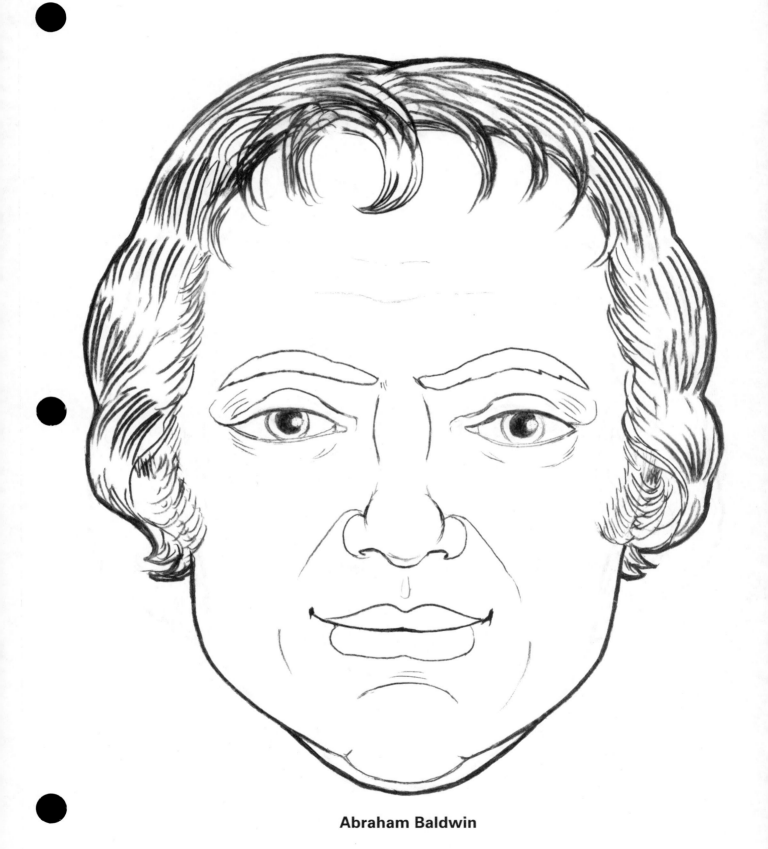

Abraham Baldwin

William Few

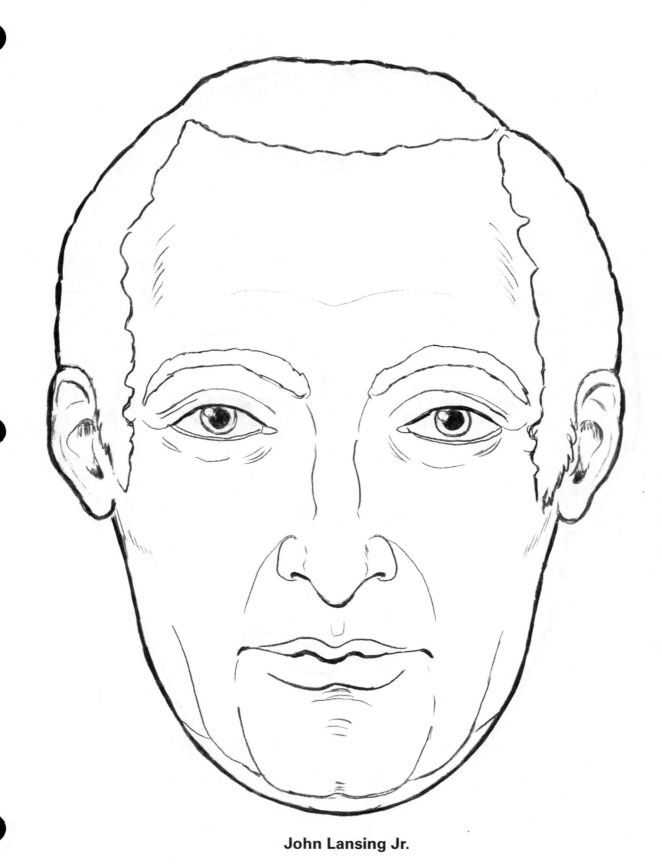

John Lansing Jr.

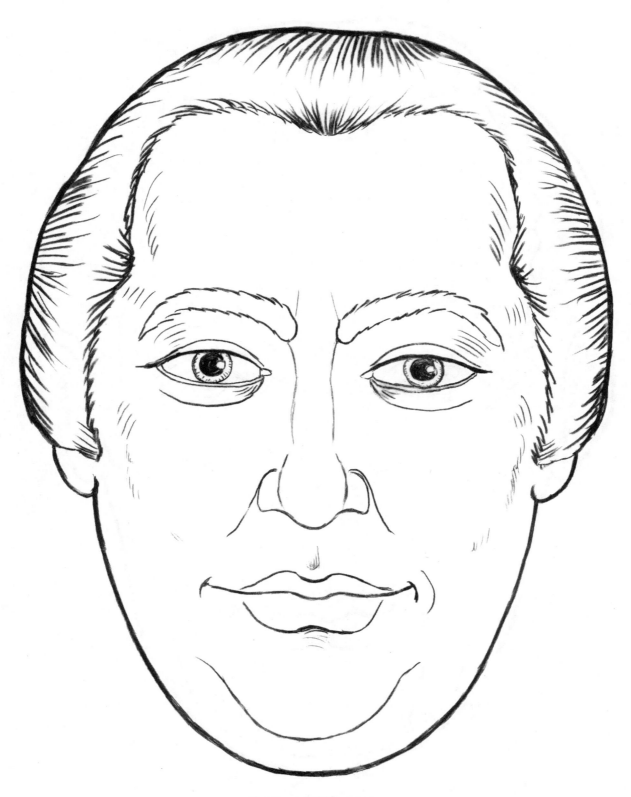

Nathaniel Gorham

Edmund Randolph

William Samuel Johnson

Jonathan Dayton

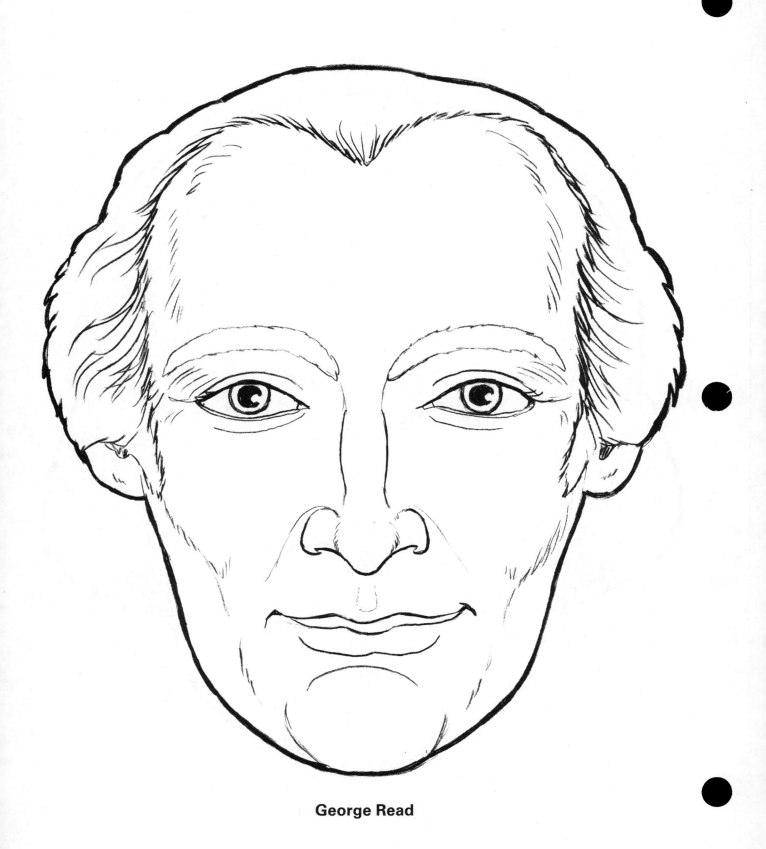

George Read

Daniel Carroll

Facsimile of the Constitution

Done in Convention by the Unanimous Consent of the States present the Seventeenth Day of September in the Year of our Lord one thousand seven hundred and Eighty seven and of the Independance of the United States of America the Twelfth *In Witness* whereof We have hereunto subscribed our Names,

Delaware
Geo: Read
Gunning Bedford jun
John Dickinson
Richard Bassett
Jaco: Broom
James McHenry

Maryland
Dan of St Thos. Jenifer
Danl Carroll.

Virginia
John Blair —
James Madison Jr.

North Carolina
Wm. Blount
Richd. Dobbs Spaight.
Hu Williamson

Done in Convention by the Unanimous Consent of the States present the Seventeenth Day of September in the Year of our Lord one thousand seven hundred and Eighty seven and of the Independance of the United States of America the Twelfth *In Witness* whereof We have hereunto subscribed our Names,

J. Rutledge

Charles Cotesworth Pinckney

Charles Pinckney

Pierce Butler

South Carolina

William Few

Abr Baldwin

Georgia

John Langdon

Nicholas Gilman

New Hampshire

Nathaniel Gorham

Rufus King

Massachusetts

Done in Convention by the Unanimous Consent of the States present the Seventeenth Day of September in the Year of our Lord one thousand seven hundred and Eighty seven and of the Independance of the United States of America the Twelfth In Witness whereof We have hereunto subscribed our Names,

Connecticut { W: Sam.l Johnson
Roger Sherman

New York ...{ Alexander Hamilton

New Jersey { W.l Livingston
David Brearley.
W.m Paterson.
Jona: Dayton

Pennsylvania { B Franklin
Thomas Mifflin
Rob.t Morris
Geo. Clymer
Tho.s FitzSimons
Jared Ingersoll
James Wilson.
Gouv Morris

Chapter 8 Assessment

Mastering the Content

Fill in the circle next to the best answer.

1. Following the American Revolution, what did Congress fear about a strong central government?
   ○ A. states would have too much power
   ○ B. rights for which people fought would be lost
   ○ C. another war would occur between Great Britain and America
   ○ D. laws would be passed to prevent people from settling in new territories

2. Which was one weakness of the Articles of Confederation?
   ○ A. Congress could not declare war.
   ○ B. Congress could not impose taxes.
   ○ C. Congress could not set up a postal system.
   ○ D. Congress could not create an army and navy.

3. What land was affected by the Land Ordinance of 1785?
   ○ A. land north and south of the colonies
   ○ B. land of the 13 original colonies
   ○ C. land bound by the Ohio and Mississippi rivers and the Great Lakes
   ○ D. land between the Mississippi River and Rocky Mountains

4. What was the long-term effect of the Northwest Ordinance of 1787?
   ○ A. Territories eventually became states.
   ○ B. The farmers of Massachusetts rebelled.
   ○ C. George Washington was elected president.
   ○ D. Slavery was expanded in the United States.

5. Why is Shays's Rebellion an important event in U.S. history?
   ○ A. It was the beginning of a civil war.
   ○ B. It led to the passage of a new Constitution.
   ○ C. It showed the strength of the Massachusetts militia.
   ○ D. It dramatized the power of the central government.

6. What was the original purpose of the convention in May 1787?
   ○ A. to write the U.S. Constitution
   ○ B. to end the conflict in Massachusetts
   ○ C. to revise the Articles of Confederation
   ○ D. to rewrite the Declaration of Independence

7. Why is James Madison known as the "Father of the Constitution"?
   ○ A. He wrote the first draft of the Constitution.
   ○ B. He knew more about government than anyone else present.
   ○ C. He was the oldest delegate to the Constitutional Convention.
   ○ D. He was well prepared to lead the discussion at the convention.

8. Which of these was the **greatest** challenge for the delegates at the Constitutional Convention?
   - ○ A. how to respond to the interests of foreign countries
   - ○ B. how to address the concerns of farmers and ranchers
   - ○ C. how to balance the interests of large and small states
   - ○ D. how to get agreement between the eastern and western states

9. The delegates to the Constitutional Convention agreed to establish a republic. Which of these describes a republic?
   - ○ A. a country led by a president
   - ○ B. a government led by a powerful few
   - ○ C. a parliamentary form of government
   - ○ D. a country led by elected representatives

10. Which of these did both the Virginia and New Jersey Plans include?
    - ○ A. an end to slavery
    - ○ B. an elected president
    - ○ C. two houses of Congress
    - ○ D. three branches of government

11. What did the Great Compromise decide?
    - ○ A. representation in Congress
    - ○ B. the names of political parties
    - ○ C. the system of checks and balances
    - ○ D. process of selecting the president

12. The number of members of which of these is affected by state population?
    - ○ A. Senate
    - ○ B. Supreme Court
    - ○ C. president's cabinet
    - ○ D. House of Representatives

13. What was the **greatest** concern of the opponents to the Constitution?
    - ○ A. taxation would be eliminated
    - ○ B. selection of George Washington as president
    - ○ C. replacement of the Articles of Confederation
    - ○ D. giving up state power to form a stronger Union

14. The delegates to the Constitutional Convention gave the job of choosing a chief executive to
    - ○ A. all the citizens.
    - ○ B. members of Congress.
    - ○ C. electors chosen by the states.
    - ○ D. state legislatures and governors.

15. Which of these describes a federal system of government?
    - ○ A. Government is run by one political party.
    - ○ B. A single leader makes all of the government decisions.
    - ○ C. Individual states have power over the national government.
    - ○ D. Power is shared by the national and state governments.

16. What was the position of the group known as the Federalists?
    - ○ A. They supported the new constitution.
    - ○ B. They questioned the justice of slavery.
    - ○ C. They feared the power of the national government.
    - ○ D. They believed that states should have equal representation in Congress.

Applying Social Studies Skills
Use the graphs and your knowledge of history to answer these questions.

Graph 1: Population of U.S. States, 1790

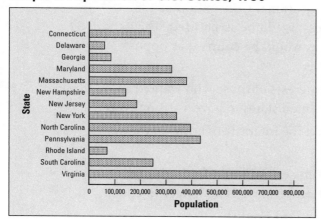

Graph 2: Comparative Populations of Southern States, 1790

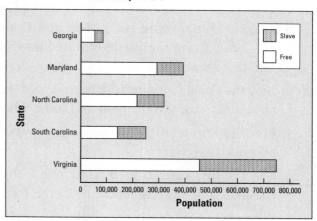

17. How did the states in Graph 2 want each slave to be counted in determining representation?
    - ○ A. as property to be taxed
    - ○ B. as three-fifths of a person
    - ○ C. the same as any other person
    - ○ D. the same as cattle and horses

18. Based on Graph 2, which state stood to gain the most representatives in Congress if slaves were counted?

19. Based on Graphs 1 and 2, which state—New York or Maryland—would have more representatives if slaves were counted?

    Which state—New York or Maryland—would have more representatives if slaves were **not** counted?

Exploring the Essential Question

What compromises emerged from the Constitutional Convention?

Follow the directions to complete the item below.

20. Compromise was key to the success of the Constitutional Convention of 1787. The Great Compromise established how Congress would be structured. The Three-Fifths Compromise determined how slaves would be counted as population. In a short, three-paragraph essay, describe

    • how the Great Compromise represented the interests of those who wanted a strong national government and those who wanted states to have a strong voice.

    • how the Three-Fifths Compromise represented the interests of both southern and northern states.

    • why the structure set up by the Great Compromise is still in effect today while the structure established by the Three-Fifth Compromise is no longer in effect.

    Make sure to convey your ideas clearly, using standard English.

Constitutional Exam Cards

Set 1 Legislative Branch (Section 9.3)

Legislative Branch

1 What is the length of a term of office for members of the U.S. House of Representatives?

Legislative Branch

2 How old must a person be to be elected to the U.S. House of Representatives? To the Senate?

Legislative Branch

3 Who has the power to propose a law to raise revenue (a tax law)?

Legislative Branch

4 Who has the power to declare war?

Set 2 Executive Branch (Section 9.4)

Executive Branch

5 What is the length of a term of office for the president of the United States?

Executive Branch

6 Who has the power to nominate ambassadors, Supreme Court justices, and other U.S. officials?

Executive Branch

7 Who is the commander in chief of the U.S. military forces?

Executive Branch

8 What are the citizenship requirements to run for president?

Set 3 Judicial Branch (Section 9.5)

Judicial Branch

9 For how long can a Supreme Court justice serve?

Judicial Branch

10 When a crime is committed in a particular state, where is the trial held?

Judicial Branch

11 Does a state or a federal court try cases dealing with disputes between states?

Judicial Branch

12 An ambassador is the highest-ranking U.S. official who represents the United States in a foreign country. Which court hears cases dealing with ambassadors?

Set 4 Check and Balances (Section 9.6)

Checks and Balances

13 What can Congress do if the president vetoes a bill?

Checks and Balances

14 Who must approve the president's appointments for ambassadors, Supreme Court justices, and other U.S. officials?

Checks and Balances

15 Who must approve a treaty made with a foreign country?

Checks and Balances

16 Which branch has the power to decide whether laws are constitutional?

Set 5 Amendment Process (Section 9.7)

Amendment Process

17 Who has the power to propose amendments to the Constitution?

Amendment Process

18 Who approves amendments to the Constitution?

Amendment Process

19 Which amendment sets the term limit for the presidency?

Amendment Process

20 Which amendment gives 18-year-olds the right to vote?

Set 6 Federal System (Section 9.8)

Federal System

21 What is the supreme law of the land?

Federal System

22 What does the full faith and credit clause do?

Federal System

23 Who has the power to regulate interstate commerce?

Federal System

24 Who has the power to print and coin money?

Constitutional Law Exam

Obtain the envelope with the Constitutional Exam Cards for the section you are
working on. In the corresponding space below, answer the question on each card
in a complete sentence. Also record the article and section number from the
Constitution where the answer can be found.

Legislative Branch (Section 9.3)

1.

2.

3.

4.

Executive Branch (Section 9.4)

5.

6.

7.

8.

Judicial Branch (Section 9.5)

9.

10.

11.

12.

Checks and Balances (Section 9.6)

13.

14.

15.

16.

Amendment Process (Section 9.7)

17.

18.

19.

20.

Federal System (Section 9.8)

21.

22.

23.

24.

Taking the Constitutional Law Exam

Follow these steps to complete your Constitutional Law exam.

Step 1: Working with your partner, read your assigned section. Complete the Reading Notes for that section.

Step 2: Send one partner to get the envelope for the section.

Step 3: Choose a card from the envelope and read the question aloud. Use your book, Reading Notes, and the Constitution (in the back of your book) to answer the question. Then record your answer on your Constitutional Law Exam. Repeat this step for each card in the envelope.

Step 4: After you have answered all the cards in your envelope, raise your hand to indicate that you are ready for your teacher to check your answers.

Step 5: Repeat Steps 1 to 4 until you have completed the Reading Notes and the exam questions for each of Sections 9.3 to 9.5.

Law School Diplomas

TCI Law School

on the nomination of the Faculty of the School of Law

has submitted

_____

to the degree of Juris Doctor

Magna Cum Laude

with all the rights and privileges

thereto pertaining.

TCI Law School

on the nomination of the Faculty of the School of Law

has submitted

_____

to the degree of Juris Doctor

Magna Cum Laude

with all the rights and privileges

thereto pertaining.

Chapter 9 Assessment

Mastering the Content

Fill in the circle next to the best answer.

1. Why is the U.S. Constitution called a "living document"?
   - ○ A. It has changed with time.
   - ○ B. It is rewritten by each president.
   - ○ C. It has remained the same over the years.
   - ○ D. It is signed each year by members of Congress.

2. Why did the delegates start the Preamble to the Constitution with the words "We, the people"?
   - ○ A. to record that all the citizens wrote the Constitution
   - ○ B. to state that government power comes from the people
   - ○ C. to declare that the people were separating from Great Britain
   - ○ D. to provide an introduction that would interest readers

3. What is the primary work of Congress?
   - ○ A. to make laws for the country
   - ○ B. to debate whether laws are constitutional
   - ○ C. to determine who will be the candidate for president
   - ○ D. to be the chief executives of the states they represent

4. What is the final step before a national bill becomes a law?
   - ○ A. It is signed by the president.
   - ○ B. It is voted on by the citizens.
   - ○ C. It is passed by the Supreme Court.
   - ○ D. It is approved by the state legislators.

5. Why does each state have two senators?
   - ○ A. to balance the rights of large and small states
   - ○ B. so the Senate does not become overcrowded
   - ○ C. to assure there are enough people to pass the laws
   - ○ D. so that one can take over if the other is unavailable

6. What is the purpose of the system of checks and balances?
   - ○ A. to list the responsibilities of elected officials
   - ○ B. to make it difficult to amend the Constitution
   - ○ C. to prevent any one branch from becoming too powerful
   - ○ D. to share power between state and national governments

7. All of these are duties of the executive branch **except**
   - ○ A. negotiating treaties.
   - ○ B. carrying out the laws.
   - ○ C. proposing new taxes.
   - ○ D. nominating federal judges.

8. Why does the Constitution establish the principle of majority rule?

    ○ A. so decisions are based on what the president wants
    ○ B. so decisions represent what most of the people want
    ○ C. so decisions are made only when more than half of the people vote
    ○ D. so decisions are made when most of the members of Congress are present

9. Which of these describes the responsibility of the judicial branch?

    ○ A. to put laws into effect
    ○ B. to resolve disputes under the law
    ○ C. to veto decisions of the Supreme Court
    ○ D. to propose bills needed to achieve justice

10. What name is given to the Supreme Court's power to declare a law unconstitutional?

    ○ A. federalism
    ○ B. veto power
    ○ C. impeachment
    ○ D. judicial review

11. The U.S. population can directly participate in government in all of these ways **except** through

    ○ A. passing laws.
    ○ B. joining interest groups.
    ○ C. participating in elections.
    ○ D. belonging to political parties.

12. Which of these powers is shared by state and national governments?

    ○ A. raising taxes
    ○ B. declaring war
    ○ C. printing money
    ○ D. negotiating treaties

13. Which of these refers to the sharing of power between national and state governments?

    ○ A. bicameral
    ○ B. federalism
    ○ C. commerce
    ○ D. nationalism

14. An amendment to the Constitution can be ratified by three-fourths of the

    ○ A. Senate.
    ○ B. citizens.
    ○ C. state legislatures.
    ○ D. Supreme Court justices.

15. Which of these can propose an amendment to the Constitution?

    ○ A. Congress
    ○ B. governors
    ○ C. presidents
    ○ D. Supreme Court

16. All of these are advantages to having states share a common market **except** that

    ○ A. it creates a single national economy.
    ○ B. trade outside of the country is prohibited.
    ○ C. a large business can be located in several states.
    ○ D. goods and resources can move more easily across the country.

Applying Social Studies Skills

Use the diagram and your knowledge of history to answer these questions.

Constitutional Checks and Balances

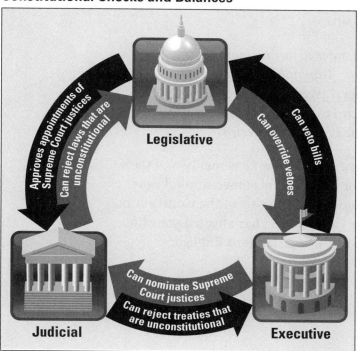

17. How does the president balance the power of Congress?

18. How does the Supreme Court prevent the president and Congress from abusing their power?

19. How does Congress check the power of the president?

Exploring the Essential Question

How has the Constitution created "a more perfect Union"?

Follow the directions to complete the item below.

20. Read the Preamble to the U.S. Constitution.

> *We, the People of the United States, in order to form a more perfect Union, <u>establish Justice</u>, <u>insure domestic Tranquility</u>, <u>provide for the common defence</u>, <u>promote the general Welfare</u>, and <u>secure the Blessings of Liberty</u> to ourselves and our Posterity, do ordain and establish this Constitution for the United States of America.*

In a two-paragraph essay, explain how the Constitution has met two of the five goals underlined above in your life or in the life of someone you know. Include details that show your understanding of the goals of the Constitution as outlined in the Preamble and how the Constitution has affected your life. Also make sure to convey your ideas clearly, using standard English.

Chapter 10 Assessment

Mastering the Content
Fill in the circle next to the best answer.

1. In 1788, why did several states refuse to approve the U.S. Constitution?
   - ○ A. It did not list the rights of the people.
   - ○ B. It did not include the branches of government.
   - ○ C. It did not indicate who would be the chief executive.
   - ○ D. It did not allow for changes to be made in the future.

2. Which of these best describes James Madison's role in the creation of the Bill of Rights?
   - ○ A. judge
   - ○ B. author
   - ○ C. reporter
   - ○ D opponent

3. Which of these is one purpose of the Bill of Rights?
   - ○ A. to determine the election process
   - ○ B. to limit the power of government
   - ○ C. to rewrite the Constitution
   - ○ D. to outline the responsibilities of Congress

4. Which of these describes Thomas Jefferson's belief about government and religion?
   - ○ A. He believed religion should guide government policy.
   - ○ B. He believed in the separation of religion and government.
   - ○ C. He believed taxes should pay for the construction of churches.
   - ○ D. He believed that only members of a religion should serve as president.

5. What is included in the First Amendment to the Constitution?
   - ○ A. the basic freedoms of all people
   - ○ B. the three branches of government
   - ○ C. the structure of the federal system
   - ○ D. the responsibilities of the president

6. Which of these groups is responsible for protecting the rights listed in the Bill of Rights?
   - ○ A. president
   - ○ B. governors
   - ○ C. federal courts
   - ○ D. representatives

7. Which of these is not included in the First Amendment?
   - ○ A. freedom to vote
   - ○ B. freedom of speech
   - ○ C. freedom of religion
   - ○ D. freedom to assemble

8. Examine the table.

Second Amendment	Right to bear arms
Third Amendment	Right to refuse the quartering of troops in homes
Fourth Amendment	Protection against searches and seizures

To which of these experiences did these three amendments respond?
   - ○ A. slavery in America
   - ○ B. American Indian relocation
   - ○ C. British rule in colonial America
   - ○ D. immigrant treatment in America

9. How does freedom of the press help maintain a democratic society?

○ A. It provides jobs for journalists.
○ B. It allows citizens to be informed.
○ C. It prevents politicians from giving opinions.
○ D. It requires newspapers to charge a low price.

10. Which of these would **not** be protected by the First Amendment?

○ A. criticizing officials in an editorial
○ B. debating controversial issues in class
○ C. promoting ideas that are unpopular
○ D. damaging property in a protest march

11. Examine the table.

Ninth Amendment	Rights retained by the people
Tenth Amendment	Powers reserved to the states

Why are these two amendments included in the Bill of Rights?

○ A. to prevent the addition of rights
○ B. to give states the power to limit rights
○ C. to allow for changes to the Constitution
○ D. to keep a balance of power and rights

12. Which of these is a responsibility of the right to freedom of the press?

○ A. to tell the truth
○ B. to print every day
○ C. to write creatively
○ D. to interview celebrities

13. Which of these guarantees that a group has the right to gather to protest a tax they think is unfair?

○ A. the right to privacy
○ B. the right to assemble
○ C. the right to bear arms
○ D. the right to worship freely

14. The Second Amendment is often at the center of debate in this country. Which of these rights does it protect?

○ A. the right to own guns
○ B. the right to pay taxes
○ C. the right to public education
○ D. the right to vote in elections

15. What is meant by the "due process of law" included in the Fifth Amendment?

○ A. The government must follow rules as it carries out the law.
○ B. If you are accused of a crime, the law does not guarantee your rights.
○ C. If you are accused of a crime, the law requires you to pay a fine.
○ D. The government cannot deny freedom to convicted criminals.

16. What does the Ninth Amendment say about rights not listed in the Constitution?

○ A. There are rights beyond those listed.
○ B. Rights not listed do not exist according to the law.
○ C. Rights not listed must be added to be considered rights.
○ D. The rights listed are the only ones approved by the states.

Applying Social Studies Skills

Use the table and your knowledge of social studies to answer these questions.

Legal Rights and Protections in the Bill of Rights

Before being charged with a crime, you are protected from • a search of your property without a search warrant. • arrest by the police without a warrant or good reason.	After an arrest, you have the right to • remain silent when questioned. • talk to a lawyer. • have a grand jury hearing to weigh the evidence against you.	Once indicted, you have the right to • know the charges against you. • reasonable bail. • a speedy trial. • a jury trial.
At your trial, you have the right to • question witnesses against you. • call witnesses in your defense. • refuse to answer questions that could harm you. • be defended by a lawyer.	If found innocent, you are protected from • double jeopardy.	If found guilty, you are protected from • excessive fines. • cruel or unusual punishments.

17. Which group is **most** affected by the rights and protections listed in the table?
   - ○ A. immigrants
   - ○ B. government workers
   - ○ C. people accused of a crime
   - ○ D. people who are unemployed

18. Read the statement below.

   Once a person is found guilty of a crime, he or she no longer has any rights.

   Based on the information in the table, is this a factual statement? Write a sentence to support your answer.

19. Which words in the table show that a person's right to privacy is protected?

Exploring the Essential Question

What freedoms does the Bill of Rights protect and why are they important?

Follow the directions to complete the item below.

20. When the first Congress met in 1789, some representatives did not think adding a Bill of Rights to the Constitution was necessary. Suppose you are one of the representatives who support amending the Constitution to add a list of the people's rights. In a short, three-paragraph essay, persuade your fellow representatives to approve the addition of the Bill of Rights. In your essay, include

    • your reasons for wanting the Bill of Rights to be included.

    • a brief scenario that (1) points out the importance of one of the amendments and (2) explains how it will affect people's lives.

    Make sure to convey your ideas clearly, using standard English.

Unit 3 Timeline Challenge Cards

Articles of Confederation Adopted
1781

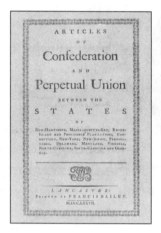

The states adopt the Articles of Confederation as the first plan of government for the United States. The plan is too weak to be effective.

Shays's Rebellion
Aug. 1786–Feb. 1787

In Massachusetts, a rebellion of farmers shows the weakness of the new U.S. government under the Articles of Confederation.

Northwest Ordinance
1787

Congress passes the Northwest Ordinance as the plan under which the Northwest Territory will be governed. The law also establishes the process for admitting new states to the Union.

Constitutional Convention Opens
May 1787

Delegates from 12 states meet in Philadelphia, Pennsylvania, and create a new plan of government that becomes the U.S. Constitution. George Washington leads the convention.

The Great Compromise
July 1787

Proposed by Roger Sherman, the Great Compromise is accepted by the Constitutional Convention. Under this plan, representation in the House of Representatives is based on each state's population. In the Senate, each state has equal representation.

The Federalist Papers
Oct. 1787

Leaders who support ratification of the Constitution, including James Madison, begin publishing a series of essays explaining how the Constitution would create a stronger union of states.

U.S. Constitution Adopted
June 1788

The U.S. Constitution is adopted after having been ratified by 9 of the 13 states. It becomes the supreme law of the United States and provides the framework for the organization of government.

Bill of Rights Adopted
Dec. 1791

Nine of the 13 states ratify the Bill of Rights, which becomes the first 10 amendments to the Constitution.

Preview Songs

Hail, Columbia

Hail, Columbia, happy land!
Hail, ye heroes, heav'n-born band,
Who fought and bled in freedom's cause,
Who fought and bled in freedom's cause,
And when the storm of war was gone
Enjoy'd the peace your valor won.
Let independence be our boast,
Ever mindful what it cost;
Ever grateful for the prize,
Let its altar reach the skies.

Firm, united let us be,
Rallying round our liberty,
As a band of brothers joined,
Peace and safety we shall find.

Immortal patriots, rise once more,
Defend your rights, defend your shore!
Let no rude foe, with impious hand,
Let no rude foe, with impious hand,
Invade the shrine where sacred lies
Of toil and blood, the well-earned prize,
While off'ring peace, sincere and just,
In Heaven we place a manly trust,
That truth and justice will prevail,
And every scheme of bondage fail.

Firm, united let us be,
Rallying round our liberty,
As a band of brothers joined,
Peace and safety we shall find.

Columbia: another name for the United States of America

valor: the qualities of a hero

impious: without respect

Fair and Free Elections

While some on rights and some on wrongs
Prefer their own reflections,
The people's rights demand our song—
The right of free elections.

For government and order's sake
And laws' important sections
Let's all stand by the ballot box
For freedom of elections.

Law and order be the stake
With freedom and protection
Let all stand by the ballot box
For fair and free elections.

Each town and county's wealth and peace,
Its trade and all connections.
With science, arts must all increase
By fair and free elections.

Then thwart the schemes of fighting lands
And traitor disaffections.
Stand up with willing hearts and hands
For fair and free elections.

Law and order be the stake
With freedom and protection
Let's all stand by the ballot box
For fair and free elections.

Should enemies beset us round
Of foreign fierce complexions.
Undaunted we can stand our ground
Upheld by free elections.

Elections are to make us laws,
For trade, peace and protection.
Who fails to vote forsakes the cause
Of fair and free elections.

Law and order be the stake
With freedom and protection
Let all stand by the ballot box
For fair and free elections.

Hamilton and Jefferson Masks

Alexander Hamilton

Thomas Jefferson

Talk-It-Out Prompts

Issue 1: Views of Human Nature

People are selfish! For that reason we can't give too much power to the common people.

Alexander Hamilton

The common people are the best suited to govern because . . .

Thomas Jefferson

Issue 2: Views on Government

The national government should have limited powers and leave Americans alone!

Thomas Jefferson

The best form of government is one that . . .

Alexander Hamilton

Issue 3: Views on the Economy

The ideal economy is based on industry!

Alexander Hamilton

The real way to expand our economy is . . .

Thomas Jefferson

Issue 4: Views on Great Britain and France

You Federalists are a bunch of British bootlickers! We need to continue to support France.

Thomas Jefferson

The new French rulers are barbarians! We should stay close to Great Britain because . . .

Alexander Hamilton

Chapter 11 Assessment

Mastering the Content
Fill in the circle next to the best answer.

1. All of these were part of President Washington's cabinet **except** the
   - ○ A. Department of War.
   - ○ B. Department of State.
   - ○ C. Treasury Department.
   - ○ D. Education Department.

2. What is an excise tax?
   - ○ A. a tax on property
   - ○ B. a tax on income earned
   - ○ C. a tax on the production or sale of a product
   - ○ D. a tax on money inherited or received as a gift

3. What was the cause of the Whiskey Rebellion?
   - ○ A. Farmers refused to pay taxes on whiskey.
   - ○ B. Farmers refused to use grain to produce whiskey.
   - ○ C. The government would not allow the trade of whiskey.
   - ○ D. The government made the production of whiskey illegal.

4. Why did President Washington order the army to end the Whiskey Rebellion?
   - ○ A. He feared the citizens would start another revolution.
   - ○ B. He felt it was his responsibility to protect tax collectors.
   - ○ C. He saw the rebellion as a threat to the new government's authority.
   - ○ D. He was more comfortable as a military leader than a political leader.

5. What advice did President Washington give to Americans in his Farewell Address?
   - ○ A. Pay taxes without complaint.
   - ○ B. Support the revolution in France.
   - ○ C. Do not address the president with royal titles.
   - ○ D. Do not let political party loyalty divide the nation.

6. All of these occurred in President Washington's administration **except**
   - ○ A. the nation was at peace.
   - ○ B. the country grew in size.
   - ○ C. political parties were eliminated.
   - ○ D. cabinet members were selected.

7. Which of these was a major issue dividing the Federalist and Republican parties?
   - ○ A. how to divide the nation's wealth equally
   - ○ B. how many terms a president should serve in office
   - ○ C. how large and powerful the military should be
   - ○ D. how large and powerful the federal government should be

8. What did Alexander Hamilton believe was important for the United States to become a great nation?
   - ○ A. a strong economy
   - ○ B. agricultural growth
   - ○ C. a partnership with France
   - ○ D. powerful state governments

9. Republicans believed that the U.S. economy should be based on

○ A. trade.
○ B. business.
○ C. agriculture.
○ D. manufacturing.

10. Why did most Republicans support the French Revolution?

○ A. They believed democracy was worth the fight.
○ B. They admired the orderliness of the revolution.
○ C. They admired the strength of the French monarchy.
○ D. They believed the wealthy were best prepared to lead France.

11. Why did most Federalists favor good relations with Great Britain?

○ A. They feared their military power.
○ B. They depended on their business.
○ C. They wanted to be protected by them.
○ D. They hoped to move there someday.

12. According to Alexander Hamilton, how would a national bank serve the country's interests?

○ A. It would eliminate the need for taxes.
○ B. It would provide loans to businesspeople.
○ C. It would create jobs for U.S. citizens.
○ D. It would be a place for foreign countries to deposit money.

13. Which of these was one of the ways Republicans viewed the Alien and Sedition Acts?

○ A. as a tool to remove political parties
○ B. as a way to increase citizen's rights
○ C. as an attack on the right of free speech
○ D. as a necessity to keep order in the new nation

14. Based on the states' rights theory of the Constitution, what does each state have the authority to do?

○ A. nullify federal law
○ B. choose the president
○ C. rewrite the Bill of Rights
○ D. increase the number of U.S. senators

15. Which of these events led to the addition of the Twelfth Amendment to the Constitution?

○ A. the election of 1800
○ B. the Whiskey Rebellion
○ C. the Alien and Sedition Acts
○ D. the establishment of a national bank

16. Why did Jefferson call the election of 1800 a peaceful revolution?

○ A. Fighting in France ended.
○ B. Slaves were able to vote for the first time.
○ C. Serious differences were resolved without violence.
○ D. Those who opposed his election moved out of the country.

Applying Social Studies Skills

Use the passage below and your knowledge of history to answer these questions.

[The election] being now decided by the voice of the nation, announced according to the rules of the Constitution, all will, of course, arrange themselves under the will of the law, and unite in common efforts for the common good . . . And let us reflect that . . . we have yet gained little if we countenance [allow] a political intolerance as despotic [tyrannical], as wicked, and capable of as bitter and bloody persecutions . . . But every difference of opinion is not a difference of principle. We have been called by different names brethren of the same principle. We are all Republicans, we are all Federalists . . . I believe this [to be] the strongest Government on earth.

—Thomas Jefferson, First Inaugural Address, March 4, 1801

17. Why did President Jefferson include the words "We are all Republicans, we are all Federalists" in his address?

18. What event caused President Jefferson to include the words "We are all Republicans, we are all Federalists" in his address?

19. Jefferson said, "But every difference of opinion is not a difference of principle." Which of the following is a principle with which most Americans agreed?
   - A. that the Constitution can never be changed
   - B. that the U.S. president can make no mistakes
   - C. that the U.S. economy should be based on business
   - D. that the United States is an independent, free nation

Exploring the Essential Question

How did the Federalist and Republican visions for the United States differ?

Follow the directions to complete the item below.

20. Determine whether each characteristic listed in the chart below was typical of a Federalist or of a Republican. Place a check in the appropriate column.

Characteristic	Federalist	Republican
Farmer		
Believes the wealthy should rule		
Supports the French Revolution		
Believes in a strong national government		

Now, based on your knowledge of each party, briefly describe the type of person you would expect to be a member of each of these political parties. Use the chart as a guide, but include at least one additional characteristic that distinguishes a person from that party.

Make sure to convey your ideas clearly, using standard English.

Description of a typical Federalist:

Description of a typical Republican:

Chapter 12 Assessment

Mastering the Content

Fill in the circle next to the best answer.

1. As stated in his Farewell Address, which term **best** describes President Washington's foreign policy?
   - ○ A. aggression
   - ○ B. isolationism
   - ○ C. colonial expansion
   - ○ D. alliance expansion

2. Which of these events challenged the foreign policy of President Adams?
   - ○ A. attacks on U.S. ships
   - ○ B. refusal of France to pay loans
   - ○ C. Spanish invasion of the country
   - ○ D. British policies toward African Americans

3. What did the Jay Treaty accomplish in 1796?
   - ○ A. The United States bought land from Spain.
   - ○ B. The British agreed to support the French Revolution.
   - ○ C. The United States reserved land for American Indians.
   - ○ D. The British removed their troops from the Ohio Valley.

4. Which slogan portrayed the U.S. response to the XYZ Affair?
   - ○ A. Free trade and sailors' rights!
   - ○ B. No taxation without representation!
   - ○ C. Millions for defense, but not one cent for tribute!
   - ○ D. First in war, first in peace, first in the hearts of his countrymen!

5. Which country was **most** responsible for the change in U.S. foreign policy at the end of the 18th century?
   - ○ A. Spain
   - ○ B. Mexico
   - ○ C. Canada
   - ○ D. Great Britain

6. Which of these was an important achievement of John Adams's administration?
   - ○ A. The nation was at peace.
   - ○ B. The country grew in size.
   - ○ C. The Federalist Party grew strong.
   - ○ D. The alliances with other countries were strengthened.

7. After going to war with each other, why did Great Britain and France seize U.S. merchant ships?
   - ○ A. They hoped to force the United States into the war.
   - ○ B. They hope the United States would become their ally.
   - ○ C. They wanted the United States to pay a ransom for their ships.
   - ○ D. They hoped to prevent the United States from supplying their enemy.

8. Who was hurt **most** by Jefferson's embargo on trade?
   - ○ A. France
   - ○ B. Great Britain
   - ○ C. North African pirates
   - ○ D. American sea workers

9. Which of these actions increased tension between the United States and Great Britain in 1807?
   - ○ A. U.S. taxes on British goods
   - ○ B. British killing of 21 U.S. sailors
   - ○ C. U.S. limits on British immigration
   - ○ D. British demand for money to protect U.S. ships

10. Why were the War Hawks eager to go to war with Great Britain in 1812?
    - ○ A. They hoped to build a stronger navy.
    - ○ B. They hoped to drive the British out of Canada.
    - ○ C. They wanted revenge for Great Britain's colonial policies.
    - ○ D. They wanted to end the British blockade of U.S. ports.

11. What could have prevented the Battle of New Orleans?
    - ○ A. stronger armies
    - ○ B. better leadership
    - ○ C. faster communication
    - ○ D. thoughtful negotiations

12. All of these were results of the War of 1812 **except**
    - ○ A. the United States won the war.
    - ○ B. the power of the Federalists decreased.
    - ○ C. national pride in the United States grew.
    - ○ D. American Indian resistance in the Northwest Territory weakened.

13. Which event led to the policies established by the Monroe Doctrine?
    - ○ A. the pirating of ships in North Africa
    - ○ B. the competition for trade between countries
    - ○ C. the wars between Great Britain and France
    - ○ D. the independence movement in Latin America

14. Who advised President Monroe that the United States should boldly speak for itself on its policy in the Americas?
    - ○ A. James Madison
    - ○ B. Andrew Jackson
    - ○ C. Thomas Jefferson
    - ○ D. John Quincy Adams

15. What was a goal of the Monroe Doctrine?
    - ○ A. to put an end to attacks on U.S. ships
    - ○ B. to warn against impressment of U.S. sailors
    - ○ C. to encourage foreign trade with European merchants
    - ○ D. to prevent European interference in North and South America

16. What was a result of the Monroe Doctrine?
    - ○ A. The United States gained respect.
    - ○ B. The United States went to war with France.
    - ○ C. The United States allied with European nations.
    - ○ D. The United States lost its image as a democratic leader.

Name_____ Date_____

Applying Social Studies Skills

Use the Great Seal of the United States and your knowledge of history to answer these questions.

17. Which symbol on the Great Seal represents peace, and which symbol represents war?

18. The banner bears the words *E PLURIBUS UNUM,* which means "From many, one." Briefly explain why these words are included on the Great Seal.

19. How is the Great Seal used?

Exploring the Essential Question

To what extent should the United States have become involved in world affairs in the early 1800s?

Follow the directions to complete the item below.

20. Between the administrations of George Washington and James Monroe, the United States changed its foreign policy from non-involvement in foreign affairs to involvement in foreign affairs. Describe the foreign policy of each of these presidents. In your descriptions, include two conditions or events that contributed to each president's foreign policy.

    Then describe which foreign policy you think should have been followed in the early 1800s. Support your answers with historical facts.

    Make sure to convey your ideas clearly, using standard English.

    Foreign policy of President George Washington:

    Foreign policy of President James Monroe:

    Your opinion on which foreign policy would have been best for the United States in the early 1800s:

Visiting an Art Exhibit in the Early 1800s

Welcome to an early 1800s art exhibit! Follow these steps to view five pieces of art from this period.

Step 1: Read Section 13.4. Complete the second and third columns of the matrix in your Reading Notes by listing two characteristics of each style or artist and drawing a symbol.

Step 2: Go to your assigned station and examine the placard.

Step 3: Using the information from your Reading Notes, determine which art style or artist relates to the placard. Complete that row of your matrix.

Step 4: Discuss this question with your partner: *What makes this piece American?* Record your response in the last cell of that row.

Step 5: Move to another placard, and repeat the procedure.

Attending a Cotillion in the Early 1800s

Welcome to the cotillion! Follow these steps to take part in this early 1800s dance.

Step 1: Read Section 13.5. Complete the corresponding Reading Notes.

Step 2: Join with another pair to form a group of four.

Step 3: Your teacher will give your group an illustration of three dance steps as they appeared in an early 1800s dance book. Practice performing the steps with your group.

Step 4: Move the desks aside to clear a large, open space in the middle of the room.

Step 5: When your teacher tells you to, form a large circle.

Step 6: While the music is playing, your teacher will call out the number of each group in turn. When your group's number is called, go to the center of the circle and perform your dance steps. Then quickly move back to the outside of the circle.

Dance Steps to the Cotillion

Group 1	Group 2	Group 3

1 Asking to dance

1 Leading out

1 Hornpipe

2 Leading out

2 Down the middle

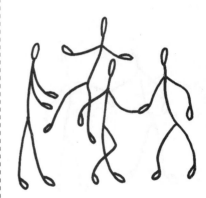

2 Right and left

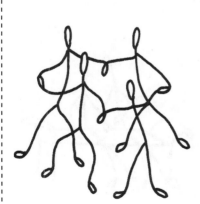

3 Hands four round

3 Right and left

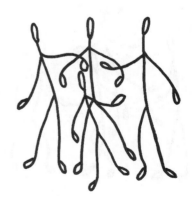

3 Cross hands

Adapted from Vera Brodsky Lawrence, *Music for Patriots, Politicians, and Presidents.*

Group 4	Group 5	Group 6

1 Asking to dance	**1** Down the middle	**1** Hornpipe
		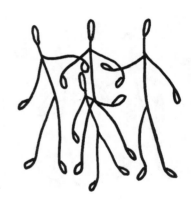
2 Leading out	**2** Pousette	**2** Cross hands
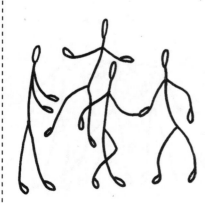		
3 Right and left	**3** Hands four round	**3** Tête-à-tête

Group 7	Group 8	Group 9

1 Down the middle	**1** Leading out	**1** Leading out
	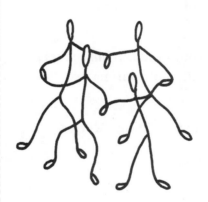	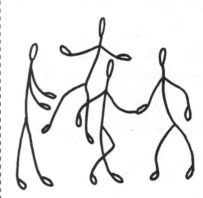
2 Right and left	**2** Hands four round	**2** Right and left
	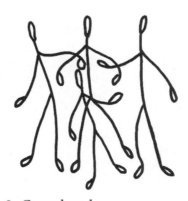	
3 Fainting	**3** Cross hands	**3** Fainting

Attending a Literary Gathering in the Early 1800s

Welcome to an early 1800s literary gathering! Follow these steps to share excerpts from four literature works of this period.

Step 1: Read Section 13.6. Complete the second and third columns of the matrix in your Reading Notes.

Step 2: Join with another pair to form a group of four.

Step 3: Cut the literature excerpts from Student Handout 13B and give each group member one excerpt.

Step 4: Have one group member read the first excerpt aloud. Use your Reading Notes and book to help you determine the title and author of the piece. Record your answer in the corresponding column of your matrix.

Step 5: Discuss this question with your group: *What makes this excerpt American?* Record your response in the last column of your matrix.

Step 6: Repeat Steps 4 and 5 with the remaining excerpts.

Excerpts from Literature of the 1800s

Excerpt A

We came from the place where the sun is hid at night, over great plains where the buffaloes live, until we reached the big river. There we fought the Alligewi, till the ground was red with their blood. From the banks of the big river to the shores of the salt lake, there was none to meet us. The Maquas followed at a distance. We said the country should be ours from the place where the water runs up no longer, on this stream, to a river twenty suns' journey toward the summer . . . We drove the Maquas into the woods with the bears. They only tasted salt at the licks; they drew no fish from the great lake: we threw them the bones.

Excerpt B

We were out two weeks, and in that time killed fifteen bears. Having now supplied my friend with plenty of meat, I engaged occasionally again with my hands in our boat building and getting staves. But I at length couldn't stand it any longer without another hùnt. So I concluded to take my little son, and cross over the lake, and take a hunt there. We got over, and that evening turned out and killed three bears, in little or no time. The next morning we drove up four forks, and made a sort of scaffold, on which we salted up our meat, so as to have it out of the reach of the wolves, for as soon as we would leave our camp, they would take possession.

Excerpt C

It was one by the village clock,
When he galloped into Lexington.
He saw the gilded weathercock
Swim in the moonlight as he passed,
And the meeting-house windows, black and bare,
Gaze at him with a spectral glare,
As if they already stood aghast
At the bloody work they would look upon.

It was two by the village clock,
When he came to the bridge in Concord town.
He heard the bleating of the flock,
And the twitter of birds among the trees,
And felt the breath of the morning breeze
Blowing over the meadow brown.
And one was safe and asleep in his bed
Who at the bridge would be first to fall,
Who that day would be lying dead,
Pierced by a British musket ball.

Excerpt D

It was toward evening that Ichabod arrived at the castle of the Heer Van Tassel, which he found thronged with the pride and flower of the adjacent country. Old farmers, a spare leather-faced race, in homespun coats and breeches, blue stockings, huge shoes, and magnificent pewter buckles. Their brisk, withered little dames, in close crimped caps, long waisted shortgowns, homespun petticoats, with scissors and pin-cushions, and gay calico pockets hanging on the outside . . .

And now the sound of the music from the common room, or hall, summoned to the dance . . .

Ichabod prided himself upon his dancing as much as upon his vocal powers. Not a limb, not a fibre about him was idle.

Creating a Chapter of a Book

Suppose you are Alexis de Tocqueville, the 25-year-old Frenchman who traveled the United States from 1831 to 1832. During your visit, you created the first draft of a book about U.S. politics and culture.

You are about to return to France when you realize you have lost a chapter of your manuscript. You are thankful you still have your field notes.

Re-create your lost chapter on Americans' growing national identity. The chapter should be written from the perspective of a European and answer this question: *What did it mean to be an American in the early 1800s?* Use your Reading Notes and book to help you.

Your chapter should be five pages long and have these elements:

1. An introductory page with a title, introductory paragraph, and visual.
   - The introductory paragraph must contain a thesis that directly answers this question: *What did it mean to be an American in the early 1800s?*
   - Use one of these theses, or create one of your own: *Being an American means having tremendous pride in one's country. Being an American means having a sense of individualism. Being an American means promoting national unity.*

2. Three pages with paragraphs that support your thesis, and accompanying visuals.
   - Each page should have at least one paragraph and one visual.
   - Paragraphs should explore one or more of these topics: politics, art, music, or literature.
   - Each paragraph should have a topic sentence and examples that support your thesis. For example, you might explain how Davy Crockett's work reflected Americans' sense of individualism. Or you might explain how Henry Clay's American System attempted to unify the country.
   - Each paragraph should have at least one visual.

3. A final page with a conclusion where you summarize your thesis. Your conclusion should be at least one paragraph long and include a restatement of your thesis and a brief summary of the examples you used to support it.

Chapter 13 Assessment

Mastering the Content

Fill in the circle next to the best answer.

1. In the early 1800s, where did **most** Americans live?
   ○ A. in the southern states
   ○ B. in the New England states
   ○ C. west of the Mississippi River
   ○ D. east of the Appalachian Mountains

2. Which of these was an obstacle to unity in the United States in the early 1800s?
   ○ A. few waterways
   ○ B. desert landscapes
   ○ C. poor transportation
   ○ D. unexplored wilderness

3. What marked what was known as the Era of Good Feelings?
   ○ A. a strong sense of national unity
   ○ B. a rapid increase in immigration
   ○ C. the elimination of political parties
   ○ D. the expansion of national alliances

4. What was a goal of Henry Clay's American System?
   ○ A. to abolish slavery
   ○ B. to promote economic growth
   ○ C. to create a strong military force
   ○ D. to establish treaties with American Indians

5. Which was a major disagreement between John C. Calhoun and Daniel Webster?
   ○ A. the authority of the Supreme Court
   ○ B. the role of business in the economy
   ○ C. the rights of states to defy federal authority
   ○ D. the role of the executive branch of government

6. Which economic system, based on private ownership, did Henry Clay promote?
   ○ A. socialism
   ○ B. capitalism
   ○ C. communism
   ○ D. liberalism

7. All of these characterize John Marshall's Supreme Court decisions in the early 1800s **except**
   ○ A. they promoted national economic growth.
   ○ B. they reinforced the authority of business contracts.
   ○ C. they increased the power of the federal government over states.
   ○ D. they established the power of states over the federal government.

8. Which style of music was the creation of African American slaves?
   ○ A. opera
   ○ B. ballads
   ○ C. classical
   ○ D. spirituals

9. In the early 1800s, all of these were American symbols **except**
    ○ A. the U.S. flag.
    ○ B. the Capitol building.
    ○ C. the Uncle Sam figure.
    ○ D. the Statue of Liberty.

10. Which of these led to the end of an era and the beginning of political divisions in the United States?
    ○ A. the War of 1812
    ○ B. the election of 1824
    ○ C. James Monroe's presidency
    ○ D. John Marshall's Supreme Court

11. How did James Fenimore Cooper contribute to American culture?
    ○ A. He wrote books about the American frontier.
    ○ B. He told tales of his wilderness adventures.
    ○ C. He drew illustrations of American plants and animals.
    ○ D. He composed songs that portrayed life on southern plantations.

12. What gave early American art its individual identity?
    ○ A. the use of abstract forms
    ○ B. the unique subject matter
    ○ C. the depressing images of life
    ○ D. the popular use of religious symbols

13. As the United States developed its own national identity, which of these values did many Americans hold?
    ○ A. dominance
    ○ B. conformity
    ○ C. compassion
    ○ D. individualism

14. According to Henry Clay, what role did government have in encouraging economic growth?
    ○ A. building community housing
    ○ B. producing goods and services
    ○ C. owning stores and businesses
    ○ D. funding transportation projects

15. Which of these men used America's growing importance in the world as a theme of his poetry?
    ○ A. Thomas Cole
    ○ B. Gilbert Stuart
    ○ C. John James Audubon
    ○ D. Henry Wadsworth Longfellow

16. What was the setting of Washington Irving's American folktales?
    ○ A. western frontier
    ○ B. upstate New York
    ○ C. southern plantations
    ○ D. Boston, Massachusetts

Applying Social Studies Skills

Use the map and your knowledge of history to answer the questions.

North America, 1820

17. What physical feature marked the western border of the United States in 1820?

18. Between 1776 and 1820, how did the United States change?

19. Why were the people who lived west of the Appalachians often called hardy and rugged?

Exploring the Essential Question

What did it mean to be an American in the early 1800s?

Follow the directions to complete the item below.

20. Write a short essay comparing what it meant to be an American in the early 1800s with what it means to be an American today. Include specific characteristics, events, and symbols that molded an identity in the 1800s and influence your impression of an American identity today.

    Make sure to convey your ideas clearly, using standard English.

Creating Act-It-Outs About Jackson's Presidency

Your group will bring to life two images from Andrew Jackson's presidency. Your teacher will select one member of your group to play your assigned character. A reporter will then interview the characters.

Act-It-Out 1: Jackson's Inauguration

Step 1: Circle the character your group is assigned.

Farmer on the Frontier   *Banker from Philadelphia*

Step 2: Discuss these questions. Make sure everyone in your group is prepared to answer them.

- What hopes do you have for Jackson's presidency?
- What fears do you have for Jackson's presidency?
- If you have a chance to meet Jackson, what will you say to him?
- Do you think Jackson will promote democracy during his presidency? Why or why not?

Step 3: Discuss how the person who is chosen to perform can make the character come alive through facial expressions, tone of voice, and posture. Collect simple props to use during the act-it-out.

Act-It-Out 2: The Trail of Tears

Step 1: Circle the character your group is assigned.

Armed Soldier Escorting Cherokees to Indian Territory

Elderly Cherokee Woman on Horse

Cherokee Warrior on Horse

Cherokee Mother Walking

Cherokee Boy Carrying Dog

Cherokee Father Driving Wagon

Georgian Settler Living on Former Indian Land (not pictured)

Andrew Jackson (not pictured)

Step 2: Discuss these questions. Make sure everyone in your group is prepared to answer them.

- Why are American Indians being removed from their homelands?
- Do you think the policy of Indian removal is fair? Why or why not?
- How has this policy changed your life?
- Do you think this policy promotes American democracy? Why or why not?

Step 3: Discuss how the person who is chosen to perform can make the character come alive through facial expressions, tone of voice, and posture. Collect simple props to use during the act-it-out.

Andrew Jackson and the Growth of American Democracy   **161**

Chapter 14 Assessment

Mastering the Content

Fill in the circle next to the best answer.

1. From which group did Andrew Jackson receive the most support in the election of 1828?
   - A. Republicans
   - B. common people
   - C. rich upper-class
   - D. American Indians

2. What political party was formed by supporters of Andrew Jackson following the election of 1824?
   - A. Socialist
   - B. Federalist
   - C. Republican
   - D. Democratic

3. What name was given to President Jackson's practice of rewarding political supporters with government jobs?
   - A. democracy
   - B. mudslinging
   - C. the spoils system
   - D. the corrupt bargain

4. Which of these describes a tariff?
   - A. a tax on the income of workers
   - B. a tax on the purchase of property
   - C. a tax on goods produced in the United States
   - D. a tax on goods imported from outside the United States

5. What caused the nullification crisis?
   - A. removal policies
   - B. election of 1828
   - C. northern trade policies
   - D. southern opposition to tariffs

6. During the nullification crisis, what was really being tested?
   - A. the right to ignore Supreme Court decisions
   - B. the rights of states to override federal laws
   - C. the right of states to secede from the United States
   - D. the right to pass federal laws that benefited certain regions

7. Who challenged President Jackson's stance on the Bank of the United States?
   - A. Henry Clay
   - B. John Q. Adams
   - C. John C. Calhoun
   - D. Martin Van Buren

8. Why did President Jackson want to destroy the Bank of the United States?
   - A. He thought it benefited the rich over the farmers and workers.
   - B. He thought the leaders were stealing from the government.
   - C. He thought foreign countries were depositing too much money.
   - D. He thought farmers and workers were borrowing too much money.

9. What did President Jackson support instead of a large national bank?

○ A. state banks
○ B. personal banks
○ C. stock investments
○ D. interest-free loans

10. Which of these Supreme Court decisions did President Jackson ignore?

○ A. States can void federal law.
○ B. Only Congress can regulate trade.
○ C. American Indians have no land rights.
○ D. The Bank of the United States is constitutional.

11. Why did many whites call the Creek, Cherokee, Chickasaw, Choctaw, and Seminole groups the "Five Civilized Tribes"?

○ A. They had never gone to war with the white man.
○ B. They had adopted the white man's ways of life.
○ C. They had representation in an all-white Congress.
○ D. They had willingly given up their land to white settlers.

12. Why did U.S. laws support the removal of American Indians from their homelands?

○ A. to provide a better life for the tribes
○ B. to allow for westward expansion of agriculture
○ C. to encourage tribes to adopt the white man's culture
○ D. to enable Indians to establish farms in more fertile areas

13. How did the Supreme Court interpret the Indian Removal Act?

○ A. Tribes could choose to remain on their lands.
○ B. Tribes had no right to any land in the new territories.
○ C. Tribes had to abide by the decisions of the United States.
○ D. Tribes would receive rent from farmers using their land.

14. What was the intention of the Indian Removal Act of 1830?

○ A. to make treaties in which Indians traded land in the East for land in the Great Plains
○ B. to remove Indians by military force to western territories
○ C. to provide Indians with jobs to support their families
○ D. to declare war on Indians who resisted resettlement

15. Which of these is referred to as "The Trail of Tears"?

○ A. the 1828 presidential campaign
○ B. the final battle of the War of 1812
○ C. the war between the Black Hawks and army
○ D. the forced removal of Cherokees from Georgia

16. Which group was affected **most negatively** by the administration of President Jackson?

○ A. American Indians
○ B. African Americans
○ C. farmers and laborers
○ D. wealthy businessmen

Applying Social Studies Skills

Use the campaign poster and your knowledge of history to answer the questions.

Jackson Forever!
The Hero of Two Wars and of Orleans!
The Man of the People!
HE WHO COULD NOT BARTER NOR BARGAIN FOR THE
PRESIDENCY!
Who, although "A Military Chieftain," valued the purity of Elections and of the Electors, MORE than the Office of PRESIDENT itself! Although the greatest in the gift of his countrymen, and the highest in point of dignity of any in the world,
BECAUSE
It should be derived from the
PEOPLE!
No Gag Laws! No Black Cockades! No Reign of Terror! No Standing Army or Navy Officers, when under the pay of Government, to browbeat, or
KNOCK DOWN
Old Revolutionary Characters, or our Representatives while in the discharge of their duty. To the Polls then, and vote for those who will support
OLD HICKORY
AND THE ELECTORAL LAW.

Collection of the New-York Historical Society. Negative #8838.

17. Which group of people is the campaign poster trying to reach?

18. Which words in the poster describe Andrew Jackson?

19. Name one historical event referred to in the poster.

Exploring the Essential Question

How well did President Andrew Jackson promote democracy?

Follow the directions to complete the item below.

20. President Andrew Jackson's enemies saw him as a president hoping to become a king. Write an essay indicating your agreement with this statement or, if you disagree with this statement, your belief that he promoted democracy. Provide three specific examples from Jackson's life to support your opinion.

    Make sure to convey your ideas clearly, using standard English.

Unit 4 Timeline Challenge Cards

Washington Becomes President
1789

George Washington is inaugurated as the nation's first president.

Bank of the United States
1791

Congress forms the Bank of the United States, the idea of Treasury Secretary Alexander Hamilton, a Federalist who wanted a strong national government.

Whiskey Rebellion
1794

President Washington successfully ends the Whiskey Rebellion, a domestic revolt against a tax on whiskey.

Washington's Farewell Address
1796

Before leaving office in 1797, George Washington calls for a foreign policy of isolationism, stressing that the United States should not entangle itself in other nations' affairs.

Adams Becomes President
1797

John Adams, a Federalist, defeats Thomas Jefferson, a Republican, to become the nation's second president.

Alien and Sedition Acts
1798

The controversial Alien and Sedition Acts, which target immigrants and traitors, are signed into law by President Adams. Republicans are outraged by the acts.

Jefferson Becomes President
1801

Thomas Jefferson becomes the nation's third president. Jefferson believed in a limited national government.

Madison Becomes President
1809

James Madison takes office. His presidency is characterized by a feeling of national unity.

War of 1812
1812–1815

At Madison's request, Congress declares war against Great Britain to protect U.S. sailors at sea and to drive the British out of the northwest.

Monroe Doctrine
1823

President James Monroe declares that the Western Hemisphere is no longer open to European colonization.

Jackson Becomes President
1829

Andrew Jackson becomes president, ushering in a new era of government known as Jacksonian Democracy and extending democratic rights to the common people.

Trail of Tears
1838–1839

Under the Indian Removal Act, thousands of Cherokee Indians die when they are forced to leave their homelands and journey to Indian Territory.

The Louisiana Territory Act-It-Out

Follow the narration below to create an act-it-out about the Louisiana Territory. When your teacher says *Action!,* the actors will move, act, and speak as described. When your teacher says *Audience!,* the audience members will gasp loudly and in unison.

Locations: Your teacher will point out the locations of Washington, D.C., the Louisiana Territory, Appalachian Mountains, Mississippi River, and New Orleans on the floor map, as well as France east of the map.

Characters and starting positions: two American farmers (east of the Appalachians), President Jefferson (Washington, D.C.), James Monroe (stay seated), French foreign minister (France)

Narration

- In the year 1800, France controlled the territory of Louisiana, which included the port city of New Orleans. Many **American farmers** were moving into and settling the region between the Appalachian Mountains and the Mississippi River. *(Action!)*

- These **farmers** worked hard tending and harvesting their crops. *(Action!)*

- When it came time for **farmers** to sell their crops, they would load them on boats and float them down the Mississippi River to New Orleans. *(Action!)*

- Once in New Orleans, the **farmers** would load the crops onto ships and send them to markets in cities on the East Coast or in Europe. *(Action!)*

- France had plans to settle Louisiana on the other side of the Mississippi with their own farmers. *(Audience!)*

- **American farmers** looked across the Mississippi, where French farmers might someday settle, and began to panic. They feared that only French farmers would be allowed to use the port of New Orleans to transport their crops. *(Action!)*

- **President Jefferson** understood the farmers' concerns. He called for **James Monroe** and said, "Go to France and offer to buy New Orleans for $7.5 million." *(Action!)*

- **Monroe** set sail for France. When he arrived, he presented his offer to the **French foreign minister**. *(Action!)*

- To **Monroe's** surprise, the **foreign minister** said, "I will sell all of Louisiana to you for $15 million." *(Action!) (Audience!)*

- **Monroe** was stunned. Instead of just one city, the nation would gain a piece of land as large as the entire country. "I'll take it!" he said. *(Action!)*

- Days later, **Monroe** signed the treaty that gave our nation the Louisiana Territory. *(Action!)*

Discussing U.S. Expansion

U.S. Expansion in the 1800s

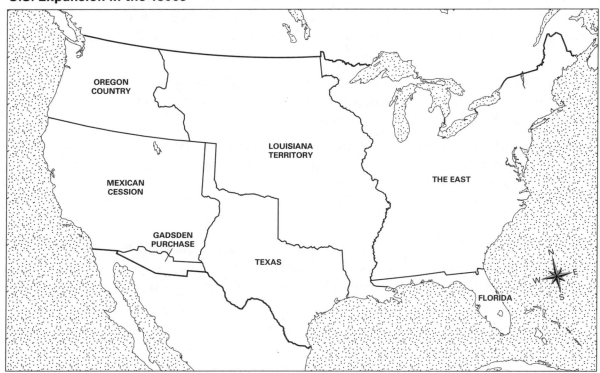

Part 1: Discuss these questions in your group, and then take a class vote.

Question A: Was U.S. expansion into the Louisiana Territory justifiable?

Question B: Was U.S. expansion into Florida justifiable?

Question C: Was U.S. expansion into Texas justifiable?

Question D: Was U.S. expansion into Oregon Country justifiable?

Question E: Was U.S. expansion after the Mexican-American War justifiable?

Part 2: Discuss the question below with your group, and decide where your answer belongs on the spectrum. Prepare a spokesperson to explain and defend your position. When your teacher calls on your group, have your spokesperson begin by saying, *[Name of previous spokesperson], our group agrees/disagrees with your group's position because . . .*

How justifiable was U.S. expansion in the 1800s?

| Totally unjustified | Mostly unjustified | Mixed | Mostly justified | Totally justified |

© Teachers' Curriculum Institute

Florida Act-It-Out

Follow the narration below to create an act-it-out about Florida. When your teacher says *Action!*, the actors will move, act, and speak as described. When your teacher says *Audience!*, the audience members will say "Govern or get out!" loudly and in unison.

Locations: Your teacher will point out the locations of Florida, Georgia, and Washington, D.C., on the floor map.

Characters and starting places: Seminole Indian (Florida), slave (Georgia), President Monroe (Washington, D.C.), General Jackson (stay seated), two cabinet members and John Quincy Adams (seated together near Washington, D.C.)

Narration

- In the early 1800s, Florida was controlled by Spain. Sometimes **Seminole Indians** from Florida would cross the border, raid U.S. lands, and escape back into Florida. *(Action!)*

- Sometimes **slaves** from Georgia would escape to Florida, where **Seminole Indians** would hide them.

- The Spanish government seemed to have no control over its territory. Years later, problems with the Seminoles continued. In 1818, **President Monroe** called for **General Andrew Jackson**. *(Action!)*

- **Monroe** ordered **Jackson** to chase the Seminoles back into Florida. He added, however, "Do *not* invade Florida." *(Action!)*

- **General Jackson** ignored **President Monroe's** instructions. He took his army to Florida and captured Spanish military posts. *(Action!)*

- Government officials in Spain were furious and wanted **General Jackson** punished. **President Monroe** said, "I fear there will be war between the United States and Spain." *(Action!)*

- **Monroe** went to his cabinet and asked, "What should I do?" *(Action!)*

- The **cabinet members** said, "Remove Jackson!" and demanded, "Apologize to Spain!" *(Action!)*

- One cabinet member, Secretary of State **John Quincy Adams,** disagreed. He took **President Monroe** aside and quietly explained his plan. *(Action!)*

- **Adams** convinced **Monroe** to stand firm and send a loud and clear message to Spain. *(Action!)* *(Audience!)*

- Adams's plan worked. Rather than risk war with the United States, Spain decided to get out. **Adams** sat down and wrote the treaty, which bears his name and gave us Florida. *(Action!)*

Texas Act-It-Out

Follow the narration below to create an act-it-out about Texas. When your teacher says *Action!,* the actors will move, act, and speak as described. When your teacher says *Audience!,* the audience members will say "Remember the Alamo!" loudly and in unison.

Locations: Your teacher will point out the locations of Missouri and Texas on the floor map, as well as Mexico City south of the map.

Characters and starting places: Stephen F. Austin (Missouri), two American settlers/Texans (Missouri), General Santa Anna (Mexico City)

Narration

- In 1821, **Stephen F. Austin** moved to Texas to follow his father's dream of starting a U.S. colony in this territory now controlled by Mexico. *(Action!)*

- By 1830, thousands of **American settlers** had joined Austin. Some even moved to Texas illegally. *(Action!)*

- Because of the illegal immigrants in Texas and other problems with the Americans, Mexican government officials ordered Texas closed to Americans. Some **American settlers** claimed "Unfair!" and called for revolution. *(Action!)*

- **Stephen F. Austin** calmed his fellow American settlers, now called **Texans,** and said he would travel to Mexico City to negotiate with the government. *(Action!)*

- When **Austin** arrived, he met with the new Mexican leader, **General Santa Anna**. First Austin said, "Reopen Texas." Then he said, "Make Texas its own state."*(Action!)*

- **Santa Anna** ignored him and jailed **Austin** for causing a rebellion. *(Action!)*

- Two years later, when **Austin** was released from jail, the **Texans** were still unhappy. They rose up in revolt. *(Action!)*

- Furious, **Santa Anna** and his army marched to Texas to crush the rebellion. *(Action!)*

- The worst battle for the Texans was at the Alamo, where every Texan was killed. This only spurred on American supporters, who flooded into Texas to help and cried . . . *(Audience!)*

- Just one month later, **Santa Anna** and his troops were sleeping in the afternoon near a river. *(Action!)*

- Suddenly, **Santa Anna** and his troops were awoken by the charge of the Texans. *(Audience!)* *(Action!)*

- The **Texans** won the battle and captured **Santa Anna**. *(Action!)*

- Mexican rule in Texas ended, and Texas became an independent country. Many wondered for how long, but for now the **Texans** cheered their victory and the Lone Star Republic. *(Action!)*

Oregon Country Act-It-Out

Follow the narration below to create an act-it-out about Oregon Country. When your teacher says *Action!*, the actors will move, act, and speak as described. When your teacher says *Audience!*, the audience members will say "All of Oregon or none!" loudly and in unison.

Locations: Your teacher will point out the locations of the Rocky Mountains, Washington, D.C., and Oregon on the floor map.

Characters and starting places: Jedediah Smith (Rockies), three settlers (near Washington, D.C.), James K. Polk (Washington, D.C.)

Narration

- In the early 1800s, many nations claimed Oregon Country. By 1825, however, only two nations held firm in their claim. The United States and Great Britain agreed to a peaceful joint occupation of Oregon. Circumstances would soon change, however, and some Americans would call for more. *(Audience!)*

- It was very difficult to reach Oregon in the early 1800s. In 1824, a trapper named **Jedediah Smith** was excited to find a low, flat passage through the Rocky Mountains. *(Action!)*

- Now the way was wide open for **settlers**. They heard that Oregon was a "pioneer's paradise," and many of them packed up their belongings and moved from the East to Oregon. *(Action!)*

- When **settlers** arrived in Oregon, they were thrilled by the fertile soil, amazed by the tall trees, and excited by the sunny weather. *(Action!)*

- In 1844, a man named James K. Polk ran for president. He wanted the nation to expand across North America. One of his campaign slogans was repeatedly heard throughout the nation. *(Audience!)*

- **James K. Polk** stood in front of voters and promised that the United States would one day own all of Oregon Country, even if it had to fight Great Britain for it. *(Action!)*

- Later that year, **Polk** was elected president. Americans who favored expansion celebrated. *(Audience!)*

- Once in office, Polk changed his mind. He decided it wasn't worth a war to gain all of Oregon Country. Instead, he made a deal to divide Oregon Country between the United States and Great Britain. The **settlers** in Oregon cheered for the diplomacy that secured their land. *(Action!)*

Mexican-American War Act-It-Out

Follow the narration below to create an act-it-out about the Mexican-American War. When your teacher says *Action!,* the actors will move, act, and speak as described. When your teacher says *Audience!,* the audience members will say "It is our manifest destiny!" loudly and in unison.

Locations: Your teacher will point out the locations of Washington, D.C., the Rio Grande, Nueces River, New Mexico, and California on the floor map, as well as Mexico south of the map.

Characters and starting places: President Polk (Washington, D.C.), two Mexican officials (Rio Grande), two U.S. soldiers (near Rio Grande), three more U.S. soldiers to play the U.S. Army (stay seated)

Narration

- In 1845, Mexico owned the California and New Mexico territories. **President Polk** offered to buy these territories, but Mexico refused. Polk was disappointed and began pacing the floor, trying to think of a way to gain these lands. *(Action!)*

- Relations between Mexico and the United States were strained at this time. The United States had recently annexed Texas and claimed the Rio Grande as the border. **Mexican officials** pointed to the Rio Grande and said, "The Rio Grande is in *our* land!" *(Action!)*

- These **Mexican officials** also pointed to the Nueces River and said, "You belong here, north of the Nueces River!" This conflict would only become worse. *(Action!)*

- One day in 1846, **U.S. soldiers** were patrolling along the Rio Grande. *(Action!)*

- Believing that the U.S. soldiers were on Mexican land, a group of Mexican soldiers attacked. When it was all over, 16 **U.S. soldiers** were wounded or lay dead on the ground. *(Action!)*

- When **President Polk** heard the news, he was outraged. "Mexico has invaded our land!" he declared. *(Action!)*

- Congress declared war on Mexico, and some Americans celebrated. *(Audience!)*

- The Mexican-American War raged for the next two years. First, the **U.S. army** invaded New Mexico and easily took the territory without firing a shot. *(Action!)*

- The **U.S. army** then invaded California and captured the territory with very few problems. *(Action!)*

- Next, the **U.S. army** invaded Mexico, where they faced fierce fighting. *(Action!)*

- Eventually, the Mexican army surrendered. By early 1848, the United States had won the war and gained control of half of Mexico's lands. Many Americans cheered and celebrated. *(Audience!)*

Chapter 15 Assessment

Mastering the Content

Fill in the circle next to the best answer.

1. What is the name given to the belief that the United States had the right and duty to expand across the North American continent?
   - ○ A. Manifest destiny
   - ○ B. Monroe Doctrine
   - ○ C. Great Awakening
   - ○ D. Louisiana Purchase

2. The United States acquired land in all of these ways **except**
   - ○ A. through war.
   - ○ B. through treaties.
   - ○ C. through settlement.
   - ○ D. through inheritance.

3. Before the early 1800s, which two countries claimed the Louisiana Territory?
   - ○ A. France and Spain
   - ○ B. Russia and Mexico
   - ○ C. Canada and Mexico
   - ○ D. United States and Great Britain

4. How did the Louisiana Purchase affect the United States?
   - ○ A. It led to war.
   - ○ B. It doubled the nation's size.
   - ○ C. It limited trade opportunities.
   - ○ D. It led to the discovery of a water route across the country.

5. What was one reason the United States wanted to acquire Florida?
   - ○ A. to increase the population
   - ○ B. to end raids on Georgia farms
   - ○ C. to control the Mississippi River
   - ○ D. to provide a short route to Europe

6. Why did some northerners oppose the annexation of Texas?
   - ○ A. Texas allowed slavery.
   - ○ B. Spain had a claim to Texas.
   - ○ C. Texas was too large to be a state.
   - ○ D. Spain demanded too high a price for Texas.

7. Which event occurred **before** Stephen F. Austin started a colony in Texas?
   - ○ A. Texas won its independence.
   - ○ B. Mexico declared independence.
   - ○ C. General Santa Anna was captured.
   - ○ D. The battle at the Alamo was fought.

8. Which of these was an incentive for settlers to travel to Oregon Country?
   - ○ A. gold deposits
   - ○ B. fertile farmland
   - ○ C. religious freedom
   - ○ D. Canadian citizenship

9. Which of these was a campaign slogan in President Polk's 1844 campaign?
   - ○ A. "Victory or death!"
   - ○ B. "Rough and ready!"
   - ○ C. "All of Oregon or none!"
   - ○ D. "Remember the Alamo!"

10. Why did the Tejanos resent the Americans settling in Texas?
    - ○ A. They did not allow slavery.
    - ○ B. They were settling illegally.
    - ○ C. They were unwilling to work.
    - ○ D. They demanded that they be made citizens.

11. What was Mexico's policy toward slavery in 1830?
    - ○ A. It was illegal.
    - ○ B. Farmers depended upon it.
    - ○ C. Mexico traded slaves for crops.
    - ○ D. It was a debated issue between Mexican states.

12. Which of these contributed to the start of the Mexican-American War?
    - ○ A. the Battle of Buena Vista
    - ○ B. the election of James K. Polk
    - ○ C. the U.S. invasion of California
    - ○ D. the annexation of Texas by the U.S. Congress

13. How was Mexico affected by the Treaty of Guadalupe Hidalgo?
    - ○ A. It gained valuable farmland.
    - ○ B. It increased trade opportunities.
    - ○ C. It decreased its territory by half.
    - ○ D. It provided more jobs for citizens.

14. Which of these describes President Polk?
    - ○ A. He did all he could to avoid war with Mexico.
    - ○ B. He wanted the United States to increase its territory.
    - ○ C. He worked to build friendships with border nations.
    - ○ D. He bought land that proved to be of little use to the country.

15. Which opinion was expressed by those who opposed the expansion of the United States?
    - ○ A. The United States was too crowded.
    - ○ B. The United States bullied its weaker neighbors.
    - ○ C. The United States was less safe than it was before.
    - ○ D. The United States should return territories won in battle.

16. What was gained through the Gadsden Purchase of 1853?
    - ○ A. a good railroad route to California
    - ○ B. a land grant to increase the size of Arizona
    - ○ C. an end to illegal immigration to the United States
    - ○ D. the end of a long border dispute with Mexico

Name_____ Date_____

Applying Social Studies Skills

Use the map and your knowledge of history to answer these questions.

U.S. Expansion in the 1800s

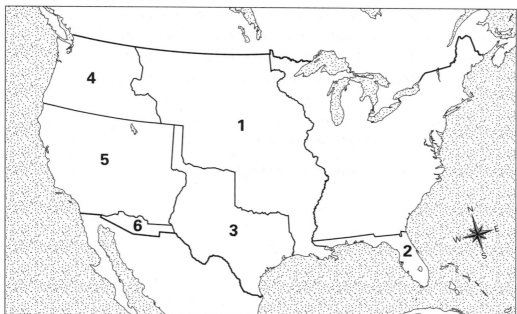

17. Briefly describe how the United States acquired the land indicated by the number 1.

18. Which two numbers indicate areas that were acquired through the treaty of Guadalupe Hidalgo?

19. What geographic feature designates the eastern border of the land indicated by the number 1?

Exploring the Essential Question

How justifiable was U.S. expansion in the 1800s?

Follow the directions to complete the item below.

20. Create two slogans relating to manifest destiny. One slogan should present a favorable viewpoint of the policy of manifest destiny; the other should present an unfavorable viewpoint. Briefly describe the viewpoint held by each slogan:

    - Under the favorable slogan, describe why the United States was justified in the expansion of the 1800s.

    - Under the unfavorable slogan, describe who or what was negatively affected by the policy of manifest destiny and how they were negatively affected.

    Make sure to convey your ideas clearly, using standard English.

Sweet Betsy from Pike

Oh, do you remember Sweet Betsy from Pike
Who crossed the wide prairie with her lover Ike?
With two yoke of oxen, a big yellow dog,
A tall Shanghai rooster, and one spotted hog.

One evening quite early they camped on the Platte,
'Twas near by the road on a green shady flat;
Where Betsy, quite tired, lay down to repose,
While with wonder Ike gazed on his Pike County rose.

The warriors came down in a wild yelling horde,
And Betsy was skeered they would scalp her adored.
Behind the front wagon wheel Betsy did crawl,
And fought off the warriors with musket and ball.

They soon reached the desert, where Betsy gave out,
And down in the sand she lay rolling about;
While Ike in great terror looked on in surprise,
Saying, "Get up now, Betsy, you'll get sand in your eyes."

They stopped at Salt Lake to inquire the way,
And Brigham invited Ike and Betsy to stay.
But Betsy declined, said, "The weather's too hot.
It's too isolated in this desert spot."

The alkali desert was burning and bare,
And Isaac's soul shrank from the death that lurked there:
"Dear old Pike County, I'll go back to you."
Says Betsy, "You'll go by yourself if you do."

The wagon tipped over with a terrible crash,
And out on the prairie rolled all sorts of trash;
A few little baby clothes done up with care,
Sweet Betsy was worried they might have a tear.

The Shanghai ran off and the cattle all died,
The last piece of bacon that morning was fried.
Poor Ike got discouraged, and Betsy got mad,
The dog wagged his tail and looked wonderfully sad.

They swam the wide rivers and crossed the tall peaks,
And camped on the prairie for weeks upon weeks.
Starvation and cholera and hard work and slaughter,
They reached California spite of hell and high water.

Chorus
Singing too rali oorali oorali ay
Singing too rali oorali oorali ay

Preparing a Minidrama About Life in the West

Your group will create and perform a minidrama to tell the story of one group of people who moved west in the 1800s. Your audience will learn your group's motives for moving west, the hardships your group faced, and the legacies they left behind. Have your teacher initial each step as you complete it.

_____ **Step 1:   Review the roles.** Make sure everyone understands the responsibilities for his or her role.

Director You will lead the group during Step 3. Make sure your storyboard contains all the required elements.

Script Manager You will lead the group during Step 4. Make sure everyone is equally involved in developing the script.

Props Manager You will lead the group during Step 5. Make sure the props and costumes will help make the minidrama realistic.

Stage Manager You will lead the group during Step 6 as group members rehearse. During the minidrama, you will direct the audience to make sound effects.

_____ **Step 2:   Learn about your western group.** Carefully examine your image and discuss what it reveals about your group. Then take turns reading aloud the section of Chapter 16 about your group. As you read, complete the Reading Notes for that section.

_____ **Step 3:   Create a storyboard that outlines your minidrama.** The Director leads the group in creating a storyboard. Your minidrama will have three scenes. The first scene will show the reasons the group moved west, the second will show the hardships they faced, and the third will show the legacies they left behind. The Director will use everyone's ideas to complete the storyboard on the third page of this handout. He or she will make sure each scene includes

- simple sketches showing each character's positions during the scene and the costumes and props to be used.
- captions describing the characters' most important actions.
- speech bubbles containing key dialogue.
- points at which the audience will participate.

_____ **Step 4: Write the script.** The Script Manager leads the group in developing the script. As you write your script, the Script Manager should make sure it

- includes a 15-second introductory statement that sets the location and time period of the first scene.
- explains your group's motives for moving to the West.
- describes the hardships your group faced.
- presents the legacies they left behind.
- allows everyone to participate equally.

Each person must make their own copy of the dialogue that the group creates.

_____ **Step 5: Prepare costumes and props.** The Props Manager leads the group in brainstorming and creating costumes and props that will make the minidrama more realistic. As you prepare materials, the Props Manager should make sure everyone has an appropriate costume or prop. During your presentation, the image will be projected on the screen behind you.

_____ **Step 6: Rehearse.** The Stage Manager leads the group in rehearsing the minidrama. You must be able to present your minidrama in five minutes or less. As you rehearse, the Stage Manager should make sure

- the presentation flows smoothly.
- costumes and props are used effectively.
- lines are spoken clearly, at an appropriate volume, and with dramatic emphasis.
- the audience participates by providing at least two sound effects.

Storyboard for Your Minidrama

Scene 1: Reasons your group of settlers moved west

Scene 2: Hardships your group faced

Scene 3: Legacies your group left behind

Chapter 16 Assessment

Mastering the Content

Fill in the circle next to the best answer.

1. Which of these led to the Lewis and Clark expedition in 1804?
   - ○ A. Monroe Doctrine
   - ○ B. Gadsden Purchase
   - ○ C. Louisiana Purchase
   - ○ D. Treaty of Guadalupe Hidalgo

2. Which of these were important to the survival of the members of the Lewis and Clark expedition?
   - ○ A. mountain men
   - ○ B. the U.S. military
   - ○ C. American Indians
   - ○ D. settlers traveling west

3. Which of these was one legacy of the Lewis and Clark expedition?
   - ○ A. They mapped a route to the Pacific.
   - ○ B. They explored present-day Colorado.
   - ○ C. They established missions in new territories.
   - ○ D. They located a water route across the country.

4. In the 1830s, what was California's main industry?
   - ○ A. fur trading
   - ○ B. coal mining
   - ○ C. shipbuilding
   - ○ D. cattle ranching

5. Who were the ancestors of the Californios?
   - ○ A. French
   - ○ B. British
   - ○ C. Spanish
   - ○ D. Canadians

6. Which is another name for the mountain men?
   - ○ A. fur trappers
   - ○ B. gold miners
   - ○ C. cattle ranchers
   - ○ D. sheep shearers

7. What was one legacy of the Californios?
   - ○ A. city names
   - ○ B. trading posts
   - ○ C. athletic events
   - ○ D. religious practices

8. What was an important legacy of the early missionaries to Oregon?
   - ○ A. They found a cure for measles.
   - ○ B. They opened the west for settlers.
   - ○ C. They converted American Indians.
   - ○ D. They traveled to the Pacific Ocean.

9. What did pioneer women achieve well before women in the East?
   ○ A. They joined the military.
   ○ B. They voted in elections.
   ○ C. They had college educations.
   ○ D. They earned wages equal to those of men.

10. What did Biddy Mason achieve in the West?
    ○ A. She owned and operated a gold mine.
    ○ B. She opened the first college for women.
    ○ C. She legally won her freedom from slavery.
    ○ D. She was the first female Mormon preacher.

11. Which of these was one effect of the California gold rush?
    ○ A. California grew in size.
    ○ B. California achieved statehood.
    ○ C. California went to war with Mexico.
    ○ D. California lost much of its population.

12. Which of these describes the experience of many Chinese immigrants in California?
    ○ A. They had to return to China after a year.
    ○ B. They were highly successful gold miners.
    ○ C. They were subjected to prejudice and abuse.
    ○ D. They were respected for their ancient culture.

13. What was one contribution of Chinese immigrants to the United States?
    ○ A. mapmaking
    ○ B. sport traditions
    ○ C. political systems
    ○ D. cultural diversity

14. Why did the Mormons move west to Utah?
    ○ A. to escape poverty and debt
    ○ B. to settle on land provided by the government
    ○ C. to convert American Indians to their religion
    ○ D. to settle where they could freely practice their beliefs

15. Which of these is a legacy of John Frémont and Zebulon Pike?
    ○ A. They found the Northwest Passage.
    ○ B. They discovered gold on a farm in California.
    ○ C. They inspired settlers to move to the West.
    ○ D. They explored the territory bordered by Canada.

16. Which of these was a challenge for many people who traveled to the West?
    ○ A. Great Plains
    ○ B. Missouri River
    ○ C. Pacific Ocean
    ○ D. Rocky Mountains

Applying Social Studies Skills

Use the map and your knowledge of history to answer these questions.

The Oregon and Mormon Trails

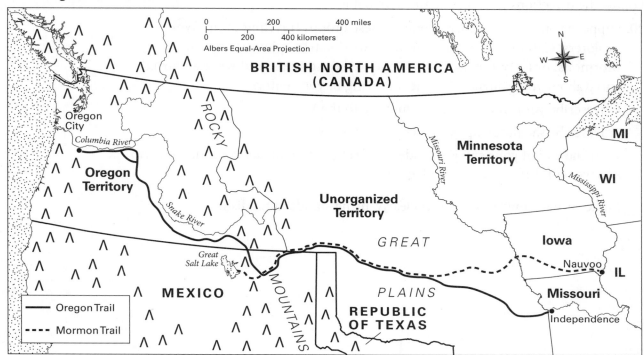

17. What physical feature created the greatest hardship for settlers traveling on the Oregon and Mormon Trails?

18. What was the final destination of the Mormons?

19. Briefly describe how the trails of the two groups differed.

Exploring the Essential Question

What were the motives, hardships, and legacies of the groups that moved west in the 1800s?

Follow the directions to complete the item below.

20. Suppose you are a member of one of these groups traveling to the West: explorers, Californios, mountain men, missionaries, pioneer women, Mormons, or forty-niners. Choose one of these groups, and write a journal entry about your journey. Do the following in your entry:

   • Describe your motivations for moving to the West.

   • Describe the hardships you faced along the way.

   • At the end of your entry, include a note about the impact your journey will have on future generations (legacy).

   Make sure to convey your ideas clearly, using standard English.

Examining Mexicano Contributions

Follow these steps to learn about Mexicano contributions and their influences.

Step 1: With your partner, go to one of the placards. Carefully examine the image, and discuss Questions 1 and 2 on the placard.

Step 2: Find the appropriate section of your Reading Notes, and write your answers to Question 2 in the second column. Then check the correct answers on the back of the placard. Circle any of your answers that match.

Step 3: Discuss Question 3 with your partner. Then return to your seats. Read the corresponding section in your book, and complete the Reading Notes for that section.

Repeat Steps 1 to 3 with a new placard.

Chapter 17 Assessment

Mastering the Content

Fill in the circle next to the best answer.

1. What happened to most of the Mexican people living in the territory given up in the Treaty of Guadalupe Hidalgo?
   ○ A. They became U.S. citizens.
   ○ B. They were forced into slavery.
   ○ C. They were deported to Mexico.
   ○ D. They became illegal residents of the United States.

2. How did the Mexicanos contribute to mining in the West?
   ○ A. They were the only group willing to do the hard work.
   ○ B. They shared their knowledge and tools with other miners.
   ○ C. They owned most of the gold, silver, and copper mines.
   ○ D. They made jewelry from gold, silver, and copper.

3. How were Mexicanos treated by people who settled in the land ceded to the United States by Mexico?
   ○ A. They were denied their rights.
   ○ B. Their property was bought at a fair price.
   ○ C. Their knowledge and culture were respected.
   ○ D. They were required to move to reservations.

4. The American cowboy borrowed or learned all of these from the Mexican cowboy (vaquero) **except**
   ○ A. branding cattle.
   ○ B. ranching terms.
   ○ C. politics and law.
   ○ D. science and religion.

5. What were the origins of the U.S. traditions of the cattle industry?
   ○ A. Spain
   ○ B. France
   ○ C. Russia
   ○ D. Great Britain

6. What was a Mexicano contribution to farming in the Southwest?
   ○ A. tractors
   ○ B. day workers
   ○ C. irrigation systems
   ○ D. plowing equipment

7. What became an important industry in the Southwest because of Mexicano farming techniques?
   ○ A. fruit production
   ○ B. flower arranging
   ○ C. dairy production
   ○ D. tool manufacturing

8. What industry did the United States adopt from the Spanish?
   ○ A. forestry
   ○ B. shipbuilding
   ○ C. sheep raising
   ○ D. wheat farming

9. Which American laws were influenced by Mexican laws?
   - A. voting
   - B. mining
   - C. building
   - D. immigration

10. What was the subject of Mexican pueblo law, which was used as a basis of U.S. law?
    - A. marriage
    - B. pollution
    - C. water rights
    - D. trade restrictions

11. What was the Mexican legal doctrine of community property rights, which has been adopted by some states?
    - A. The government shares in ownership of property.
    - B. Couples share property acquired during their marriage.
    - C. The husband owns any property acquired by a married couple.
    - D. Crops grown on government property are shared with the public.

12. What Mexican building material was used in the Southwest because of its suitability in dry climates?
    - A. wood
    - B. adobe
    - C. marble
    - D. concrete

13. What do the words *stampede, canyon,* and *patio* have in common?
    - A. They are Mexican slang words.
    - B. They describe geographic features.
    - C. They are terms used only in the Southwest.
    - D. They come from Spanish and Mexican words.

14. What professional sport has its roots in Mexico?
    - A. rodeo
    - B. tennis
    - C. racing
    - D. soccer

15. Which American music form is influenced by Mexican music?
    - A. rock and roll
    - B. jazz and blues
    - C. spiritual and choral
    - D. country and western

16. What is **best** described in the flowchart?

corn tomatoes chocolate avocados	→ ←	lamb barley walnuts grapes

   - A. exchange of foods between native Mexicans and Spanish
   - B. exchange of foods between United States and Mexico
   - C. food produced in Mexico and sold in the United States
   - D. food raised only in Mexico and food raised only in the United States

Applying Social Studies Skills

Use the list below and your knowledge of history to answer these questions.

adobe	chaps	lasso	rancher
barbecue	chili	mesa	sombrero
bronco	chocolate	mesquite	tornado
buckaroo	corral	mustang	tortilla
burro	hoosegow	poncho	vamoose
chaparral	lariat	ranch	veranda

17. English-speaking people in America commonly use many of the words in the list. Briefly describe how these terms became part of the vocabulary of people in the United States.

18. Which of these words names a geographical feature found in the Southwest?
   ○ A. mesa
   ○ B. bronco
   ○ C. hoosegow
   ○ D. chaparral

19. Name an American term that you think has become a part of the vocabulary of other countries or languages. Briefly describe why you think that has occurred.

Exploring the Essential Question

How have Mexicano contributions influenced life in the United States?

Follow the directions to complete the item below.

20. Write a short essay on how life in the United States would be different without the contributions of Mexicanos. In your essay, discuss three aspects of life that would be different. Choose from these categories:

    - cultural
    - economic or industrial
    - legal
    - language

    Make sure to convey your ideas clearly, using standard English.

Unit 5 Timeline Challenge Cards

Louisiana Purchase
1803

In a diplomatic treaty made during Thomas Jefferson's administration, the United States buys the Louisiana Territory from France. The Louisiana Purchase doubles the size of the nation.

Lewis and Clark Expedition
1804–1806

Meriwether Lewis and William Clark lead an expedition to explore the Louisiana Territory, the nation's newly acquired region west of the Mississippi River.

Acquisition of Florida
1819

Spain avoids war with the United States by ceding Florida to the United States.

Lone Star Republic Founded
1836–1845

Following the Battle of San Jacinto in 1836, Texas wins its freedom from Mexico and remains an independent nation for 10 years.

Settlers Move West
1840–1870

Several hundred thousand settlers move west across the Oregon, California, and Mormon trails.

Annexation of Texas
1845

The United States annexes Texas, making it the 28th state in the Union.

Compromise in Oregon Country
1846

The United States chooses diplomacy over war with Great Britain in order to acquire the lower half of Oregon Country.

Mexican-American War
1846–1848

Manifest destiny motivates many Americans to support war between Mexico and the United States. When the war ends, Mexico cedes half of its land, later named the Mexican Cession, to the United States.

Gold Rush
1848–1852

The discovery of gold brings 250,000 people from all over the nation and the world, including China and Europe, to California in search of wealth and opportunity.

Gadsden Purchase
1853

Seeking a good route for a railroad, the United States purchases from Mexico a narrow strip of land below Arizona. This acquisition concludes the nation's expansion across the continent.

Comstock Lode
1859

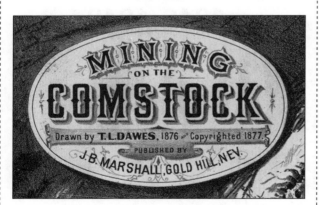

The first large deposit of silver is discovered with the help of a Mexicano miner. Mexicanos continue to help develop mining techniques and industry in the West.

Women's Suffrage in Wyoming Territory
1869

Wyoming Territory becomes the first place in the nation to give women the right to vote.

Reflecting on the Declaration of Sentiments

You will work with your group to analyze three excerpts from the Declaration of Sentiments, the document created at the Seneca Falls Convention.

Excerpt A

He has never permitted her to exercise her inalienable [undeniable] right to the elective franchise [vote]. He has compelled her to submit to laws, in the formation of which she had no voice.

Step 1: Rewrite Excerpt A, using simpler language that a classmate would understand. In the excerpt, "he" refers to the general male population of the United States.

Step 2: Discuss the extent to which this grievance has been redressed today. Place an X on the spectrum to show your response.

Not Redressed   Somewhat Redressed   Totally Redressed

Step 3: List evidence from the mid-1800s and today that supports your placement. Use your book and Student Handout 18B to help you.

Step 4: Prepare a spokesperson to defend your placement to the class.

Excerpt B

He has monopolized [dominated] nearly all the profitable employments, and from those she is permitted to follow, she receives but a scanty remuneration [pay].

Step 1: Rewrite Excerpt B, using simpler language.

Step 2: With your group, discuss the extent to which this grievance has been redressed today. Place an X on the spectrum to show your response.

Not Redressed   Somewhat Redressed   Totally Redressed

Step 3: List evidence from the mid-1800s and today that supports your placement.

Step 4: Prepare a new spokesperson to defend your placement.

Excerpt C

He has created a false public sentiment by giving to the world a different code of morals for men and women.

Step 1: Rewrite Excerpt C, using simpler language.

Step 2: With your group, discuss the extent to which this grievance has been redressed today. Place an X on the spectrum below to show your response.

Not Redressed   Somewhat Redressed   Totally Redressed

Step 3: List evidence from the mid-1800s and today that supports your placement.

Step 4: Prepare a new spokesperson to defend your placement.

Fact Sheet on Women in the United States Today

Use these facts, in addition to the information in your book, to help you prepare for the discussions about the Declaration of Sentiments.

- Women have the right to vote in every state.

- In 2009, six of the 50 U.S. governors were women.

- In 2009, 17 of the 100 U.S. senators and 76 of the 435 House of Representatives members were women.

- As of 2010, there has never been a female president or vice president. A woman was nominated twice as a candidate for the vice presidency.

- In 1972, 26% of men and women polled said they would not vote for a woman for president. In 2007, 12% of people polled said they would be less likely to vote for a woman for president.

- In 2008, women earned approximately 78¢ for every dollar men earned.

- On average, women make $434,000 less in their lifetimes than men.

- In 2008, of the 500 largest businesses in the United States, 15.7% of the top officers were women, up from 8.7% in 1995.

- In 1980, 13% of doctors were women. In 2006, 28% of doctors were women.

- In 1983, 15% of lawyers were women. In 2007, 33% of lawyers were women.

- In 2007, 25% of computer programmers, 82% of social workers, and 59% of realtors were women.

- In 2007, 33% of women ages 25 to 29 attained a bachelor's degree or higher compared to 26% of men.

- In 1970, one in 27 girls participated in high school varsity sports. In 2008, more than one in three girls participated in high school varsity sports.

- In 2008, over 42% to 49% of high school students taking the Advanced Placement tests in calculus were female. In the same year, 59% of those taking biology and 48% of those taking chemistry were female.

Class Spectrum

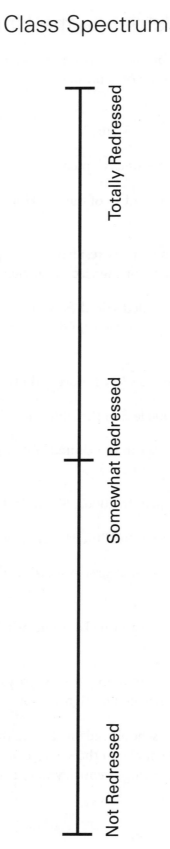

Chapter 18 Assessment

Mastering the Content

Fill in the circle next to the best answer.

1. Which of these describes a person who followed a philosophy that taught people to trust their emotions and intuition?
   ○ A. suffragette
   ○ B. abolitionist
   ○ C. expansionist
   ○ D. transcendentalist

2. Dorothea Dix dedicated her life to
   ○ A. teaching religion.
   ○ B. eliminating slavery.
   ○ C. helping the imprisoned.
   ○ D. establishing public schools.

3. Which of these describes Henry David Thoreau's approach to individualism?
   ○ A. He questioned society's rules and institutions.
   ○ B. He believed that the rule of law led to a perfect society.
   ○ C. He wanted to increase government control of citizens' lives.
   ○ D. He promoted communities in which people share everything.

4. What was the focus of Horace Mann's reform movement?
   ○ A. religion
   ○ B. health care
   ○ C. voting rights
   ○ D. public education

5. Which group benefited **most** from early efforts to establish public schools?
   ○ A. girls
   ○ B. boys
   ○ C. American Indians
   ○ D. African Americans

6. Which group was focused on eliminating slavery?
   ○ A. politicians
   ○ B. abolitionists
   ○ C. missionaries
   ○ D. transcendentalists

7. How did Frederick Douglass spread his message of freedom for all people?
   ○ A. through newspapers
   ○ B. by running for office
   ○ C. by rising up in revolt
   ○ D. through church sermons

8. What motivated William Lloyd Garrison to join the antislavery movement?
   ○ A. distinguished awards
   ○ B. political popularity
   ○ C. economic benefits
   ○ D. religious beliefs

9. Which of these was an obstacle for women who were working to end slavery in the United States?

○ A. They were not allowed to vote.
○ B. They were not allowed to attend school.
○ C. They could not voice their opinions.
○ D. They could not travel throughout the country.

10. In which way were the lives of slaves and women similar?

○ A. Both were denied rights.
○ B. Both were considered property.
○ C. Neither was paid for their work.
○ D. Neither was able to attend school.

11. Why did Elizabeth Blackwell have a difficult time getting into medical school?

○ A. There were no schools in her home state.
○ B. She could not afford to pay the tuition.
○ C. Most medical schools would not accept women.
○ D. Her grades were not considered good enough.

12. Which of these was being denied to women in 1848?

○ A. ability to attend school
○ B. freedom to raise a family
○ C. control over property and wages
○ D. opportunity to attend church services

13. What event motivated Elizabeth Cady Stanton to become active in the women's rights movement?

○ A. She was denied admission into college.
○ B. She was not able to get teaching jobs.
○ C. She was mistreated at her place of employment.
○ D. She was not allowed to speak at a convention.

14. Who was an organizer of the Seneca Falls Convention?

○ A. Lucretia Mott
○ B. Frederick Douglass
○ C. Elizabeth Blackwell
○ D. William Lloyd Garrison

15. Which of these was the model for the Seneca Falls Declaration of Sentiments?

○ A. Bill of Rights
○ B. Monroe Doctrine
○ C. Declaration of Independence
○ D. Preamble to the U.S. Constitution

16. What was an immediate effect of the Seneca Falls Convention of 1848?

○ A. It led to the end of slavery in the United States.
○ B. It proposed laws providing equal education for all.
○ C. It created an organized campaign for women's rights.
○ D. It led to the nomination of the first congresswoman.

Name_____   Date_____

Applying Social Studies Skills
Use the timeline below and your knowledge of history to answer the questions.

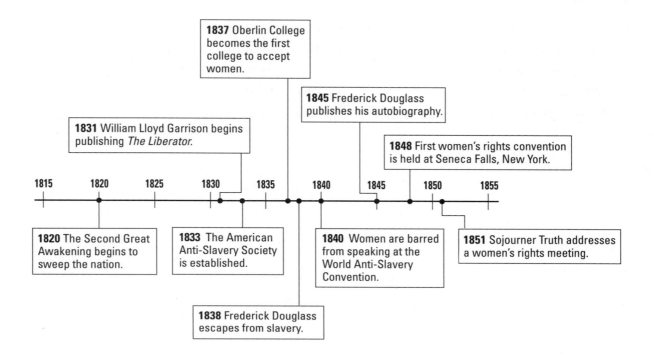

17. Which would be the **best** title for this timeline?
○ A. Reform and Reformers
○ B. Democracy in America
○ C. The Civil Rights Movement
○ D. The Second Great Awakening

18. Describe one long-term effect of the events in the timeline.

19. Based on information in the timeline, which of these can be inferred?
○ A. Women won the right to vote and slavery ended in 1851.
○ B. The majority of people who opposed slavery were women.
○ C. The women's rights movement grew out of the antislavery movement.
○ D. Frederick Douglass was the first to speak up on behalf of women's rights.

Exploring the Essential Question

To what extent did the reform movements of the mid-1800s improve life for Americans?

Follow the directions to complete the item below.

20. Think about the various reform movements discussed in this chapter. In a short essay, describe three ways in which the reform movements of the mid-1800s have affected the lives of Americans today.

    Make sure to convey your ideas clearly, using standard English.

North and South Act-It-Outs

Your group will bring to life a character in an image of the North or the South. One member of your group will play the part of your assigned character. A reporter will interview the characters.

Act-It-Out 1: The Economy of the North and the South

Step 1: Make sure everyone in your group can answer these questions from the perspective of your assigned character:

- Where are you working?
- How do most people where you live make a living?
- What new inventions have increased your productivity?
- Do you think the North or the South has a stronger economy? Why?

Step 2: Discuss how the person who is chosen to perform can make the character come alive through facial expressions, tone of voice, and posture. Then collect simple props to use during the act-it-out.

Act-It-Out 2: The Society of the North and the South

Step 1: Make sure everyone in your group can answer these questions from the perspective of your assigned character:

- Where do you live?
- Describe your way of life.
- What is the social structure like where you live?
- Would you rather live in the North or the South? Why?

Step 2: Discuss how the person who is chosen to perform can make the character come alive through facial expressions, tone of voice, and posture. Then collect simple props to use during the act-it-out.

Chapter 19 Assessment

Mastering the Content

Fill in the circle next to the best answer.

1. The geography of the South supported the growing of cash crops in all of these ways **except**
   - ○ A. it had wide, fertile coastal plains.
   - ○ B. it had access to seaports to export goods.
   - ○ C. it had fast-moving rivers as a source of power.
   - ○ D. it had plentiful rainfall and long growing seasons.

2. The economy in the South was based on which of these?
   - ○ A. mining
   - ○ B. banking
   - ○ C. agriculture
   - ○ D. shipbuilding

3. How did the invention of the cotton gin impact the South?
   - ○ A. Cotton mills moved to the South.
   - ○ B. Cotton exports to Europe declined.
   - ○ C. Cotton farmers no longer needed slaves.
   - ○ D. Cotton became the South's most important crop.

4. Which of these **best** describes the Industrial Revolution?
   - ○ A. a conflict between factory owners in cities
   - ○ B. a shift from handmade products to machine-made products
   - ○ C. a decrease in immigrant labor and an increase in slave labor
   - ○ D. a change from privately owned businesses to government-controlled businesses

5. Why did the South oppose laws to provide federal money for internal improvements, such as roads and canals?
   - ○ A. They thought taxes would need to be raised.
   - ○ B. They thought these improvements were dangerous.
   - ○ C. They thought these improvements were unnecessary.
   - ○ D. They thought these improvements would benefit only Northern states.

6. How were goods primarily transported in the South?
   - ○ A. by air
   - ○ B. by rail
   - ○ C. by river
   - ○ D. by road

7. By 1850, which of these was the **most** efficient way to move goods in the North?
   - ○ A. by railroad
   - ○ B. by steamboat
   - ○ C. by canal boat
   - ○ D. by stagecoach

8. Unlike the North, why did Southerners invest little money in mills and factories?
   - ○ A. They did not buy manufactured goods.
   - ○ B. They put their money in land and slaves.
   - ○ C. They thought mills and factories caused pollution.
   - ○ D. They preferred the lifestyle of small family farmers.

9. Why were textile mills built near rivers?

○ A. Rivers provided power to operate the mills.

○ B. Rivers provided transportation for employees of the mills.

○ C. Textile mills were built near population centers.

○ D. Textile mills provided cloth for factories near the rivers.

10. Which of these **best** describes the difference between an agrarian and an industrialist in the 1800s?

○ A. One is poor while the other is wealthy.

○ B. One employs slaves and the other employs immigrants.

○ C. One works to support a family while the other works to make money.

○ D. One favors policies that support farming and the other favors policies that support factories.

11. Which invention brought industrialization to Northern agriculture?

○ A. reaper

○ B. steamboat

○ C. power loom

○ D. sewing machine

12. What was life like for free African Americans in the North?

○ A. They were given special privileges.

○ B. They were encouraged to move to the South.

○ C. They were not treated as equal to other citizens.

○ D. They had the same rights as all other citizens.

13. Who were the political leaders in the South in the mid-19th century?

○ A. factory owners

○ B. wealthy planters

○ C. religious leaders

○ D. educated lawyers

14. Which conditions in Northern Europe encouraged emigration between 1845 and 1860?

○ A. war and famine

○ B. disease and slavery

○ C. natural disasters and climate change

○ D. religious persecution and poor education

15. Which of these was a major cause of immigration to the United States between 1845 and 1860?

○ A. political conflict

○ B. offers of free land

○ C. escape from slavery

○ D. investment opportunities

16. Which of these is one reason that U.S. immigrants settled in the North?

○ A. It offered free land.

○ B. It offered jobs in mills and factories.

○ C. They were attracted by the good climate.

○ D. They were attracted by the railroad system.

Applying Social Studies Skills

Use the map and your knowledge of history to answer these questions.

U.S. Railroads, 1860

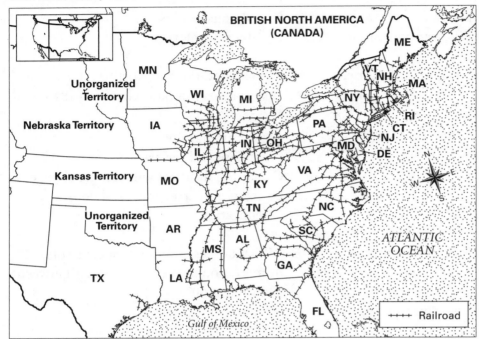

17. Based on the map, which of these statements is true?
   ○ A. Southern politicians, more than Northern politicians, supported funding for rail lines.
   ○ B. There were more railroad lines in the North than in the South.
   ○ C. Railroad lines were laid only in regions where the land was flat.
   ○ D. Northern railroad lines did not connect to Southern railroad lines.

18. At which of these locations do many of the railroad lines meet?
   ○ A. at Northern ports
   ○ B. at Southern coastlines
   ○ C. at the Gulf of Mexico
   ○ D. at the Canadian border

19. How did the railroad system affect the U.S. economy in the 1860s?

Exploring the Essential Question

How was life in the North different from life in the South?

Follow the directions to complete the item below.

20. Suppose you are a Southerner spending the summer in a Northern city in the mid-1800s. Write a letter to a family member describing how life in the North differs from your life in the South.

    In your letter, give details about four aspects of life—geography, transportation, economy, and society—that convey the contrast between the two regions. Also make sure to convey your ideas clearly, using standard English.

Analyzing Quotations and Images

In this activity, you will read quotations and examine images about the experiences of African Americans in the mid-1800s.

Step 1: Read one of the quotations aloud.

Step 2: Find the placard that best matches the topic of the quotation.

Step 3: Find the corresponding topic in your Reading Notes. Complete Questions 1 and 2.

Step 4: Read the section in your book about that topic. Then complete the Reading Notes for that section.

Step 5: Have your teacher check your work. Then exchange your quotation for a new one.

Repeat Steps 1 to 5 until you have examined all of the quotations and images and have completed your Reading Notes.

Quotations from Slaves

Quotation 1

We had old ragged huts made out of poles, and some of de cracks chinked up wid mud and moss and some of dem wasn't. We didn' have no good beds, jes' scaffolds nailed up to de wall out of poles and de ole ragged buddin' throwed on dem. Dat sho' was hard sleepin' but even dat feel good to our weary bones after dem long hard days work in de field.

—Jenny Proctor
(ex-slave, Texas)

We had old ragged huts made out of poles, and some of the cracks were filled with mud and moss, and some weren't. We didn't have any good beds, just scaffolds nailed up to the wall made out of poles and old ragged bedding thrown on them. That sure was hard sleeping, but even that felt good to our weary bones after those long hard days of work in the fields.

Jenny Proctor, interviewed in Texas (no date), in *The American Slave: A Composite Autobiography,* edited by George P. Rawick. Copyright © 1972 by George P. Rawick. Reproduced with permission of ABC-CLIO, LLC.

Quotation 2

One ob de cruelest things I ever seen done to a slave wuz done by my Master. He wanted to punish one ob de slaves what had done some 'em dat he didn't lak, a kinda stubborn one. He . . . hitched him to a plow an' plowed him jes' lak a hors. He beat him an' jerked him 'bout 'till he got all bloody an' sore, but ole Marse he kept right on day after day. Finally de buzzards went to flyin' over 'em . . . dem buzzards kept a flyin' an' old Marse got to being haunted by dat slave an' buzzards. He could alwas' see 'em an' hear de groans . . . an' he was hainted dat way de res' ob his life.

—Vinnie Busby
(ex-slave, Mississippi)

One of the cruelest things I ever saw done to a slave was done by my master. He wanted to punish one of the slaves who had done something that he didn't like. [The slave] was kind of a stubborn one. He took that slave and hitched him to a plow and plowed him just like a horse. He beat him and jerked him about until he got all bloody and sore, but the old master kept right on day after day. Finally, the buzzards were flying over them . . . those buzzards kept flying and the old master was haunted by that slave and the buzzards. He could always see them and hear the groans . . . And he was haunted that way for the rest of his life.

Vinnie Busby, interviewed in Rankin County, Mississippi (no date), in *The American Slave: A Composite Autobiography,* edited by George P. Rawick. Copyright © 1972 by George P. Rawick. Reproduced with permission of ABC-CLIO, LLC.

Quotation 3

Chorus:
Our bondage'll have an end, by and by, by and by.
Our bondage'll have an end, by and by.

Jehovah rules the tide
And the waters he'll divide,
Oh, the way he'll open wide,
By and by.

Chorus

From Egypt's yoke set free
Hail the glorious jubilee,
Oh how happy we will be
By and by.

Chorus

Our Lord will save his own
By the power from his throne,
And old Pharaoh will drown
By and by.

—from a spiritual

Quotation 4

My father wuz sold 'way from us when I wuz small. Dat wuz a sad time fer us. Mars wouldn't sell de mudders 'way from deir chillun so us lived on wid out de fear ob bein' sold. My pa sho' did hate ter leave us. He missed us and us longed fer him. He would often slip back ter us' cottage at night. Us would gahter 'round him an' crawl up in his lap, tickled slap to death, but he give us dese pleasures at a painful risk. When his Mars missed him he would beat him all de way home.

—Hannah Chapman
(ex-slave, Mississippi)

My father was sold away from us when I was small. That was a sad time for us. Master wouldn't sell the mothers away from their children, so we lived on without fear of being sold. My Pa sure did hate to leave us. He missed us and we longed for him. He would often slip back to our cottage at night. We would gather around him and crawl up in his lap, and he tickled us for a long time. But he gave us these pleasures at a painful risk. When his master missed him, he would beat him all the way home.

Hannah Chapman, interviewed in Simpson County, Mississippi (no date), in *The American Slave: A Composite Autobiography*, edited by George P. Rawick. Copyright © 1972 by George P. Rawick. Reproduced with permission of ABC-CLIO, LLC.

Quotation 5

Most times when slaves went to deir quarters at night, mens rested but sometimes dey holped de 'omans cyard de cotton and wool. Young folkses frolicked, sung songs, and visited from cabin to cabin. When dey got behind wid de field wuk, sometimes slaves wuked atter dinner Saddays, but dat warn't often. But, Oh, dem Sadday nights! Dat was when slaves got together and danced. George, he blowed de quills, and he sho could blow grand dance music on 'em . . . Dere warn't no foolishment 'lowed after ten o'clock no night. Sundays dey went to church and visited 'round, but folks didn't spend as much time gaddin' 'bout lak dey doesn now days.

—Georgia Baker
(ex-slave, Georgia)

Most of the time when slaves went to their quarters at night, men rested. But sometimes they helped the women card the cotton and wool. Young folks frolicked, sang songs, and visited from cabin to cabin. When they got behind with the fieldwork, sometimes slaves worked after dinner on Saturdays, but that wasn't often. But, oh, those Saturday nights! That was when slaves got together and danced. George played an instrument [possibly a harmonica], and he sure could blow grand dance music . . . Noisy activities were not allowed after ten o'clock on any night. Sundays they went to church and visited each other, but folks didn't spend as much time gadding about [looking for a good time] like they do nowadays.

Georgia Baker, interviewed in Athens, Georgia, 1938, in *The American Slave: A Composite Autobiography,* edited by George P. Rawick. Copyright © 1972 by George P. Rawick. Reproduced with permission of ABC-CLIO, LLC..

Quotation 6

On Sundays . . . I have seen the negroes up in the country going away under large oaks, and in secret places, sitting in the woods with spelling books. The best and the brightest were killed during Nat's time [referring to Nat Turner, a deeply religious slave who led a revolt in which nearly 60 whites were killed]. All the colored folks were afraid to pray in the time of the old prophet Nat. There was no law about it; but the whites reported it round among themselves, that if a note was heard, we should have some dreadful punishment; and after that, the low whites would fall upon any slaves they heard praying or singing a hymn, and often killed them before their masters or mistress could get to them.

—Charity Bowery
(ex-slave, North Carolina)

Charity Bowery, interviewed in New York by Lydia Marie Child, 1848, for *The Emancipator,* a weekly New York publication of the American Anti-Slavery Association. The interview is reprinted in *Slave Testimony: Two Centuries of Letters, Speeches, Interviews, and Autobiographies,* edited by John W. Blassingame (Baton Rouge, LA: Louisiana State University Press, 1977).

Quotation 7

And about this time I had a vision—and I saw white spirits and black spirits engaged in battle, and the sun was darkened—the thunder rolled in the Heavens, and blood flowed in streams . . . while labouring in the field, I discovered drops of blood on the corn as though it were dew from heaven . . . And on the 12th of May, 1828, I heard a loud noise in the heavens, and the Spirit instantly appeared to me and said the Serpent was loosened, and . . . that I should take it on and fight against the Serpent, for the time was fast approaching when the first should be last and the last should be first . . . And on the appearance of the [last] sign (the eclipse of the sun last February), I should arise and prepare myself, and slay my enemies with their own weapons.

—The Confessions of Nat Turner, 1831

Quotation 8

Uncle Big Jake sho' work de slaves from early mornin' till night. When you is in de field you better not lag none. When its fallin' weather de hands is put to work fixin' dis and dat. De women what has li'l chillen don't have to work so hard. Dey works 'round de sugar house and come 11 o'clock dey quits and cares for de babies till 1 o'clock, and den works till 3 o'clock and quits.

—Sarah Ford
(ex-slave, Texas)

Uncle Big Jake sure worked the slaves from early morning till night. When you are in the field, you'd better not lag behind. When it is raining or snowing the hands are put to work fixing this and that. The women who have little children don't have to work so hard. They work round the sugar house and at 11 o'clock they quit and care for the babies until 1 o'clock, and then they work until 3 o'clock and quit.

Sarah Ford, interviewed in Houston, Texas (no date), in *The American Slave: A Composite Autobiography,* edited by George P. Rawick. Copyright © 1972 by George P. Rawick. Reproduced with permission of ABC-CLIO, LLC..

Creating a Slave Journal

You will write three entries in a journal from the perspective of a slave living in the mid-1800s. Your entries should describe how a slave might have faced slavery and discrimination.

Entry 1: On this first page, describe yourself and your living and working conditions. Include

- a date and location, such as *November 4, 1853, Johnson Plantation, South Carolina.*
- your name, age, and a brief a description of your family.
- a description of your living conditions.
- a description of a typical workday and your working conditions.
- an illustration.

Entry 2: On the second page, describe a way in which you have resisted slavery. Include

- a date and location.
- a description of your quiet or open act of rebellion.
- an illustration.

Entry 3: On the third page, describe ways in which you and other slaves maintain a strong sense of community. Include

- a description of your favorite leisure time activity.
- a description of a church meeting.
- an illustration.

Chapter 20 Assessment

Mastering the Content

Fill in the circle next to the best answer.

1. Which is true of free African Americans living in both the North and the South?
   ○ A. They faced discrimination and racism.
   ○ B. They lived side by side with white Americans.
   ○ C. They had the same rights as everyone else.
   ○ D. They preferred living only with African Americans.

2. What was the legal status of slaves in the United States?
   ○ A. citizen
   ○ B. property
   ○ C. dependents
   ○ D. immigrants

3. What was the purpose of the National Council of Colored People?
   ○ A. to provide jobs for freed slaves
   ○ B. to encourage immigration from African nations
   ○ C. to protest the treatment of African Americans
   ○ D. to teach African Americans how to blend into white society

4. What was an effect of segregation policies in the North?
   ○ A. People shared their culture with others.
   ○ B. People were separated by race in public places.
   ○ C. People were forced to live with different races.
   ○ D. People were not allowed to practice their religion.

5. Why did Southerners who did not own slaves support slavery?
   ○ A. They feared the power of the slaveholders.
   ○ B. They believed they would be able to own slaves someday.
   ○ C. They knew that the Southern economy depended on slave labor.
   ○ D. They understood that the Constitution did not ban slavery in the South.

6. How did the cotton gin affect slaves?
   ○ A. It made their lives easier.
   ○ B. It increased the demand for slaves.
   ○ C. It decreased the need for slave labor.
   ○ D. It was the first step toward abolishing slavery.

7. What did Harriet Tubman's work with the Underground Railroad involve?
   ○ A. As a freed slave, she led others to take a stand against slave owners.
   ○ B. As a freed slave, she bought slaves and then gave them their freedom.
   ○ C. As an escaped slave, she guided slaves from the South to freedom.
   ○ D. As an escaped slave, she opened a school for those who traveled to Canada.

8. Who was Denmark Vesey?
   ○ A. a slave who escaped to Canada
   ○ B. a Northern African American abolitionist
   ○ C. a slavebreaker who punished spirited slaves
   ○ D. a free African American who lead a slave revolt

9. Who resisted slavery by organizing a violent rebellion?

○ A. Nat Turner
○ B. Edward Covey
○ C. Sojourner Truth
○ D. Frederick Douglass

10. How did Southern states respond to slave rebellions?

○ A. They gave slaves some freedom.
○ B. They passed even stricter slave codes.
○ C. They began to understand that slavery was wrong.
○ D. They refused to take slaves back when they were captured.

11. What did slaves **most** fear?

○ A. being sent back to Africa
○ B. being forced to learn new skills
○ C. being sold away from their families
○ D. being disrespectful to their owners

12. How did the "invisible church" benefit slaves?

○ A. It helped keep African languages alive.
○ B. It provided a place for slaves to plot escape.
○ C. It provided a means for slaves to comfort each other.
○ D. It helped teach children the value of silence.

13. Which of these was the **most** common way slaves resisted slavery?

○ A. by killing their owners
○ B. by escaping to the North
○ C. by organizing slave uprisings
○ D. by finding ways to quietly rebel

14. Where did free African Americans in the South **most often** find work?

○ A. on plantations
○ B. in low-paying jobs
○ C. in government jobs
○ D. on land they owned

15. Which of these **best** describes the Underground Railroad?

○ A. a series of tunnels used to move slaves to free states
○ B. people who secretly helped slaves escape to the North
○ C. a transportation system that moved slaves to freedom at night
○ D. people who caught fugitive slaves and returned them to owners

16. Slaves expressed African cultural traditions in all of the following ways **except**

○ A. through art.
○ B. through music.
○ C. through fieldwork.
○ D. through folk tales.

Applying Social Studies Skills

Use the excerpt and your knowledge of history to answer the questions.

The real feelings and opinions of the slaves were not much known or respected by their masters . . . and in this respect Col. Lloyd was no exception to the rule. His slaves were so numerous he did not know them when he saw them. Nor, indeed, did all his slaves know him. It is reported of him, that riding along the road one day he met a colored man, and addressed him . . .

"Well, boy, who do you belong to?"

"To Col. Lloyd," replied the slave.

"Well, does the Colonel treat you well?"

"No, Sir," was the ready reply.

"What, does he work you hard?"

"Yes, Sir."

"Well, don't he give you enough to eat?"

"Yes, sir, he gives me enough to eat, such as it is."

The Colonel rode on; the slave also went on about his business, not dreaming that he had been conversing with his master. He thought and said nothing of the matter, until two or three weeks afterwards, he was informed by his overseer that for having found fault with his master, he was now to be sold to a Georgia trader . . . This was the penalty of telling the simple truth.

—Frederick Douglass, in *Life and Times of Frederick Douglass*, 1881

---

17. How might Colonel Lloyd have interpreted this incident?
- ○ A. "Slaves are of no value to me."
- ○ B. "He should be grateful that I feed him well."
- ○ C. "It is important to me that my slaves like me."
- ○ D. "I must try to treat my slaves better so they are happier."

18. Why might this passage be considered a primary source?

19. Which of these describes an overseer as the word is used near the end of the passage?
- ○ A. a person who helped slaves escape
- ○ B. a person who was a slave supervisor
- ○ C. a person who bought and sold slaves
- ○ D. a person who was a spy for the slaves

Exploring the Essential Question

How did African Americans face slavery and discrimination in the mid-1800s?

Follow the directions to complete the item below.

20. In the chapter, African Americans of the 1800s were described this way: "That African Americans were neither humbled nor crushed by prejudice and discrimination was evidence of their courage and spirit."

    Write a short essay about this idea. In your essay, give four examples from the chapter that support or provide evidence of this description of the endurance of African Americans. Also make sure to convey your ideas clearly, using standard English.

Unit 6 Timeline Challenge Cards

Invention of the Cotton Gin
1793

Eli Whitney invents the cotton gin. Cotton becomes the most profitable cash crop in the South and transforms the South's economy and society.

Congress Approves National Road
1806

Congress authorizes the building of the National Road. By 1841, the road extends from Cumberland, Maryland, to Vandalia, Illinois.

Work Begins on the Erie Canal
1817

Completed in 1825, the Erie Canal provides the first all-water link between farms on the Central Plains and East Coast cities.

The Industrial Revolution
About 1820–1870

The United States undergoes an Industrial Revolution, which results in the growth of industry, urbanization, and a more modern transportation system.

Second Great Awakening
About 1800–1840

The nation experiences a revival of religious feeling that inspires many Americans to work for the improvement of society.

Founding of *The Liberator*
1831

William Lloyd Garrison starts the abolitionist newspaper *The Liberator*. In its weekly issues, he calls for the immediate freeing of all slaves.

Nat Turner's Rebellion
1831

Nat Turner leads a slave uprising in Virginia. The rebellion results in the passage of strict slave codes.

Horace Mann Campaigns for Public Schools
1837

Horace Mann becomes the Massachusetts state supervisor of education and calls for the establishment of public schools and increased pay for teachers.

Frederick Douglass Establishes *The North Star*
1847

Frederick Douglas founds *The North Star*, an antislavery newspaper. The newspaper lends support to other reform movements as well.

Seneca Falls Convention
1848

The Women's Rights Convention takes place in Seneca Falls, New York. Many participants sign the Declaration of Sentiments, which demands equal rights for women.

Harriet Tubman Escapes Slavery
1849

Harriet Tubman escapes from a slave plantation in Maryland. She later guides more than 200 slaves to freedom on the Underground Railroad.

Walden Is Published
1854

Transcendentalist Henry David Thoreau publishes *Walden*, a reflection on the meaning of life, society, nature, and the human spirit.

Creating Act-It-Outs About a Dividing Nation

Your group will bring to life images of three important events in the controversy over slavery. Your teacher will select one member of your group to play the part of your assigned character. A reporter will then interview the characters.

Act-It-Out 1: The Senate Debates California Statehood

Step 1: Circle the character your group is assigned.

Northern Senator   *Abolitionist in the Gallery*

Southern Senator   *Slave Owner in the Gallery*

Step 2: Discuss these questions. Make sure everyone is prepared to answer them.

- How do you think Congress should settle the issue of slavery?
- What do you think Congress should do about fugitive slaves?
- Should California be granted statehood? Why or why not?
- Do you think that the admission of California into the Union will keep the nation together or pull it farther apart? Why?

Step 3: Discuss how the person who is chosen to perform can make the character come alive through facial expressions, tone of voice, and posture. Use information from your Reading Notes, your book, and the image to make your character realistic. Collect simple props to use during the act-it-out.

Act-It-Out 2: Bloodshed in Kansas

Step 1: Circle the character your group is assigned.

Proslavery Settler (not pictured)   *Antislavery Settler* (not pictured)

Step 2: Discuss these questions. Make sure everyone in your group is prepared to answer them.

- What is happening here?
- Why did you move to Kansas?
- What recent events contributed to this bloodshed and to the conflict over slavery throughout the nation?
- Do you think anything can be done to keep the nation from pulling apart over the issue of slavery? Explain.

Step 3: The characters in this act-it-out will stand to the side of the projected image. Discuss how the person who is chosen to perform can make the character come alive through facial expressions, tone of voice, and posture. Use information from your Reading Notes, your book, and the image to make your character realistic. Collect simple props to use during the act-it-out.

Act-It-Out 3: The Lincoln-Douglas Debates

Step 1: Circle the character your group is assigned.

Abraham Lincoln   *Stephen Douglas*

Step 2: Prepare to deliver the statements below in a simulation of one of the Lincoln-Douglas debates. Make sure everyone in your group is prepared to be the actor.

Douglas: Ladies and gentlemen, if we allow Mr. Lincoln to have his way—that is, to abolish slavery wherever it exists—he will destroy the Union!

Lincoln: Nonsense! Let the record show that I have always said Congress does not have the right to interfere with the states and their laws, even if their laws uphold slavery. But, I do say Congress must stop the spread of slavery to the *territories*.

Douglas: Mr. Lincoln, the Dred Scott decision has settled this issue. The people in the territories—*not* Congress—have the freedom and the right to decide whether slavery will be allowed in the territories.

Lincoln: Ladies and gentleman, beware of this position. If Judge Douglas and other supporters of the Dred Scott decision have their way, slavery will become legal in every state in the Union.

Douglas: I certainly do not want to make slavery legal in any state or territory. But I also do not want to make slavery *illegal* in any state or territory. The law states that the people have the freedom to choose!

Lincoln: When Judge Douglas says he does not want to make slavery legal or illegal, he is blowing out the moral lights all around us and destroying the love of liberty in the American people. We must hold fast to the beloved principles found in the Declaration of Independence and stop the spread of slavery to the territories! I am told that our time is up. Thank you.

Step 3: Discuss the questions below. Make sure everyone can answer them so that everyone is prepared to be interviewed after the debate.

- How do Lincoln's ideas differ from Douglas's ideas?
- Who do you think will do a better job of keeping the nation together? Why?

Step 4: Discuss how the person who is chosen to perform in the debate can make the character come alive through tone of voice, facial expressions, and gestures. The actor must speak loudly and clearly and make eye contact with the audience. Collect simple props to use during the act-it-out.

Chapter 21 Assessment

Mastering the Content

Fill in the circle next to the best answer.

1. How did Missouri's application as a slave state in 1819 challenge U.S. law?
   ○ A. It did not have a state constitution.
   ○ B. States west of the Mississippi River were to be slave states.
   ○ C. It did not have the population required for statehood.
   ○ D. States north of the Ohio River were to be free states.

2. Which was a fear of Southern senators if there were more free states than slave states?
   ○ A. losing respect
   ○ B. losing tax revenue
   ○ C. losing voting power
   ○ D. losing future elections

3. What was an effect of the Missouri Compromise?
   ○ A. It temporarily ended the slavery debate.
   ○ B. It required Southern states to pay higher taxes.
   ○ C. It led to the South seceding from the Union.
   ○ D. It upset the balance of slave and free states in the Union.

4. What was the significance of the 36°30′ parallel?
   ○ A. It separated the North from the South.
   ○ B. It indicated the northern border of Missouri.
   ○ C. It showed the borders of the United States.
   ○ D. It indicated where slavery was allowed and banned.

5. According to the Wilmot Proviso of 1846, in which area was slavery banned?
   ○ A. Southern states
   ○ B. Northern states
   ○ C. Louisiana Territory
   ○ D. land acquired from Mexico

6. In what way did the Compromise of 1850 appease the South?
   ○ A. It created new taxes for railroad construction.
   ○ B. It provided an end to the slave trade in Washington, D.C.
   ○ C. It included a law requiring the return of escaped slaves.
   ○ D. It required the Underground Railway to be disbanded.

7. Which two people worked together to balance the interests of the North and the South with regard to slavery?
   ○ A. Daniel Webster and Henry Clay
   ○ B. James Polk and John Quincy Adams
   ○ C. Nat Turner and John Brown
   ○ D. Charles Sumner and Stephen A. Douglas

8. All of these were reasons the Fugitive Slave Law failed **except**
   ○ A. many slaves moved to Canada.
   ○ B. Northerners refused to obey the law.
   ○ C. hounded slave catchers returned to the South.
   ○ D. plantation owners did not want returned slaves.

9. What was the impact of the publication of *Uncle Tom's Cabin*?

○ A. It created a slave revolt in Kentucky.
○ B. It turned many more people against slavery.
○ C. Congress agreed that slavery should be abolished.
○ D. The South became more resolved to secede from the Union.

10. How did the Kansas-Nebraska Act nullify the Missouri Compromise?

○ A. It changed the borders of Missouri.
○ B. It required that all of Missouri be free.
○ C. It allowed slavery in new Northern territories.
○ D. It established new interstate trade rules.

11. Which of these was a result of the Kansas-Nebraska Act?

○ A. It led to a violent struggle over slavery in Kansas.
○ B. It settled the slavery issue in Nebraska.
○ C. It calmed the country's dispute over slavery.
○ D. It required that the new territories would be free states.

12. What was the Supreme Court's decision in the Dred Scott case?

○ A. that slavery diminished the national character
○ B. that African American rights were protected by the Constitution
○ C. that African Americans did not have the right to sue in federal court
○ D. that slavery should be abolished by executive order

13. What did John Brown hope to achieve by his raid at Harpers Ferry?

○ A. to create a slave rebellion that would bring an end to slavery
○ B. to bring attention to the conflict between the North and the South
○ C. to bring the two sides together to form a new compromise
○ D. to create a revolution that would lead to a war between the states

14. How did the Lincoln-Douglas debates of 1858 impact Lincoln's political future?

○ A. He won the senate race in Illinois.
○ B. He became known throughout the nation.
○ C. He was seen as a poor candidate for public office.
○ D. He felt discouraged and removed himself from politics for a time.

15. What was apparent following the presidential election of 1860?

○ A. The nation was divided over slavery.
○ B. Lincoln was popular throughout the nation.
○ C. There was little support for abolitionists in the North.
○ D. Southern states were eager to abolish slavery.

16. Which event turned the secession crisis into a civil war?

○ A. the election of Abraham Lincoln
○ B. South Carolina's shelling of Fort Sumter
○ C. John Brown's raid on Harpers Ferry
○ D. Preston Brooks's attack on Charles Sumner

Applying Social Studies Skills

Use the quotation and your knowledge of history to answer the questions.

> 'A house divided against itself cannot stand.' I believe this government cannot endure permanently half slave and half free. I do not expect the Union to be dissolved; I do not expect the house to fall; but I do expect it will cease to be divided. It will become all one thing, or all the other.
> —Abraham Lincoln

17. When did Abraham Lincoln speak these words?
○ A. at the Lincoln-Douglas debates
○ B. at his presidential inauguration
○ C. when he gave a campaign speech
○ D. when he accepted the senatorial nomination

18. What does the word *house* in Lincoln's statement refer to?

19. Based on his statement, which of these did Lincoln believe?
○ A. All the states will become free states.
○ B. All the states will become slave states.
○ C. The United States will not continue to be divided.
○ D. The United States will be divided into two countries.

Exploring the Essential Question

Which events of the mid-1800s kept the nation together and which events pulled it apart?

Follow the directions to complete the item below.

20. During the years prior to the Civil War, Congress made several attempts to subdue the nation's strong and divided feelings about slavery. However, these attempts often made the situation worse.

    Choose two of these events: the Missouri Compromise, the Compromise of 1850, or the Kansas-Nebraska Act. In a short essay, explain how the two events tried to bring the nation together and how these same events eventually pulled the nation further apart. Also be sure to convey your ideas clearly, using standard English.

Orders for Union Officers

You are officers of the Union camp. The Captain will give the orders below at the signal of your Commanding Officer (teacher). Read the orders in advance so that you know how to direct your soldiers. Give all orders loudly and clearly. The Lieutenant will make sure the soldiers follow the orders quickly and completely.

Order 1: "Form ranks!" *(Form two facing parallel lines. Soldiers stand side by side, shoulder to shoulder. Once the lines are formed, give the following command, emphasizing the last syllable.)*

"AttenTION!" *(Stand straight, with feet together, eyes straight ahead, arms by the sides.)*

Order 2: "Parade rest!" *(Stand with legs a little wider apart, hands clasped behind back.)*

"Soldiers, the Confederate attack may be coming at any time. Take a minute to write a short letter to your family. Fold it, address it, and tuck it inside your shirt, so we can find it if you are killed during the battle."

Order 3: "Form ranks!" *(Once lines are formed, give the following command.)*

"AttenTION!"

Order 4: When directed by the Commanding Officer, give the following speech to your troops. Use your voice, tone, and gestures to make the speech as inspiring as possible.

> *Do not hurry men . . . and fire too fast. Let them come up close before you fire, and then aim low, and steadily . . . We must hold this line* to the last man!

"Now, on the count of three, give a loud Union cheer! One, two, three!" *(If the company's cheer isn't loud enough, tell them to give it again, louder.)*

Order 5: "Form ranks!" *(Once lines are formed, give the following command.)*

"AttenTION!"

Orders for Confederate Officers

You are officers of the Confederate camp. The Captain will give the orders below at the signal of your Commanding Officer (teacher). Read the orders in advance so that you know how to direct your soldiers. Give all orders loudly and clearly. The Lieutenant will make sure the soldiers follow the orders quickly and completely.

Order 1: "Form ranks!" *(Form two facing parallel lines. Soldiers stand side by side, shoulder to shoulder. Once lines are formed, give the following command, emphasizing the last syllable.)*

"AttenTION!" *(Stand straight, with feet together, eyes straight ahead, arms by the sides.)*

Order 2: "Parade rest!" *(Stand with legs a little wider apart, hands clasped behind back.)*

"Soldiers, the orders to attack Union lines may be coming at any time. Take a minute to write a short letter to your family. Fold it, address it, and tuck it inside your shirt, so we can find it if you are killed during the battle."

Order 3: "Form ranks!" *(Once lines are formed, give the following command.)*

"AttenTION!"

Order 4: When directed by the Commanding Officer, give the following speech to your troops. Use your voice, tone, and gestures to make the speech as inspiring as possible.

> *Men, remember what you are fighting for. Remember your homes and your friends, your wives, mothers, sisters and your sweethearts.*

"Now, on the count of three, give a loud Rebel yell! One, two, three!" *(If the company's cheer isn't loud enough, tell them to give it again, louder.)*

Order 5: "Form ranks!" *(Once lines are formed, give the following command.)*

"AttenTION!"

Civil War Experience 3 Role Cards

Role Card 1: Union Doctor

When directed by the Commanding Officer (your teacher), visit your wounded soldiers *as quickly as possible*. Ask about their injuries and determine whether they are

- very serious and require *immediate* medical attention. Have the stretcher bearer help these soldiers to the field hospital at the back of the camp.

- less serious and can wait for medical attention. Tell these soldiers to move themselves to the middle of the camp and wait.

- so serious that the soldiers are already dead or cannot be saved. Have the stretcher bearer move these soldiers to the front of the camp to be buried.

Role Card 2: Confederate Doctor

When directed by the Commanding Officer (your teacher), visit your wounded soldiers *as quickly as possible*. Ask about their injuries and determine whether they are

- very serious and require *immediate* medical attention. Have the stretcher bearer help these soldiers to the field hospital at the back of the camp.

- less serious and can wait for medical attention. Tell these soldiers to move themselves to the middle of the camp and wait.

- so serious that the soldiers are already dead or cannot be saved. Have the stretcher bearer move these soldiers to the front of the camp to be buried.

Role Card 3: Union Stretcher Bearer

When directed by the Commanding Officer (your teacher), visit each of the wounded soldiers with the doctor. The doctor will ask about their injuries and determine whether they are

- very serious and require *immediate* medical attention. Help these soldiers to the field hospital at the back of the camp.

- less serious and can wait for medical attention. Tell these soldiers to move themselves to the middle of the camp and wait.

- so serious that the soldiers are already dead or cannot be saved. Move these soldiers to the front of the camp to be buried.

Role Card 4: Confederate Stretcher Bearer

When directed by the Commanding Officer (your teacher), visit each of the wounded soldiers with the doctor. The doctor will ask about their injuries and determine whether they are

- very serious and require *immediate* medical attention. Help these soldiers to the field hospital at the back of the camp.

- less serious and can wait for medical attention. Tell these soldiers to move themselves to the middle of the camp and wait.

- so serious that the soldiers are already dead or cannot be saved. Move these soldiers to the front of the camp to be buried.

Civil War Experience 3 Casualty Cards

Lie down, hold one side of your face, and moan quietly. Tell the doctor that a cannonball exploded near your face. Take a last breath, close your eyes, and die.

Lie down, hold your chest right below your heart, and moan quietly. Tell the doctor that you were shot in the chest. Take a last breath, close your eyes, and die.

Lie down, hold your stomach, and groan loudly. Tell the doctor that you were stabbed in the stomach by a bayonet and are bleeding heavily.

Lie down, put one arm inside your shirt, and groan loudly. Tell the doctor that your arm was blown off and that you are losing a lot of blood.

X

Lie down, bend one leg, and groan loudly. Tell the doctor that a cannonball crushed your leg and you are bleeding heavily.

Sit down, hold your foot, and groan loudly. Tell the doctor that a horse trampled on your foot and that you think it may be broken.

Sit down, bend two fingers in to your palm, and moan quietly. Tell the doctor that two of your fingers were shot off and that you are in great pain.

Sit down, hold your shoulder, and groan loudly. Tell the doctor that a bullet grazed your shoulder and you are bleeding from the wound.

Sit down, hold your forearm, and moan quietly. Tell the doctor that you received a sword cut on your arm and are bleeding from the wound.

X

Sit down, hold your leg, and groan loudly. Tell the doctor that a bullet passed through your leg and that the wound is very painful.

X

Chapter 22 Assessment

Mastering the Content

Fill in the circle next to the best answer.

1. Which of these was a Northern advantage at the start of the Civil War?
   - ○ A. highly trained soldiers
   - ○ B. abundant natural resources
   - ○ C. fighting in familiar territory
   - ○ D. control of the Mississippi River

2. Which of these was a Southern advantage at the start of the Civil War?
   - ○ A. large population
   - ○ B. strong military leadership
   - ○ C. control of the railway system
   - ○ D. many factories and businesses

3. Why did General Lee join the Confederate military?
   - ○ A. He was in favor of slavery.
   - ○ B. He felt loyalty to his native Virginia.
   - ○ C. He believed in the rights of states to secede.
   - ○ D. He had been defeated in the presidential election.

4. What was the significance of the Battle of Bull Run?
   - ○ A. It proved that the South was weak.
   - ○ B. It showed that the North would win.
   - ○ C. It proved that a quick victory was impossible.
   - ○ D. It showed that the armies were unwilling to fight long battles.

5. What was Jefferson Davis's role prior to becoming president of the Confederate States?
   - ○ A. He was a Northern abolitionist.
   - ○ B. He was a wealthy plantation owner.
   - ○ C. He represented Mississippi in the U.S. Senate.
   - ○ D. He was a candidate in the 1860 presidential election.

6. The Union's Anaconda Plan included all of the following strategies **except**
   - ○ A. dividing the South.
   - ○ B. blocking Southern ports.
   - ○ C. capturing Richmond, Virginia.
   - ○ D. assassinating the Confederate president.

7. What did General Lee hope would be the result of sending his troops to fight on Union soil?
   - ○ A. A show of strength in Maryland might convince the state to join the Confederacy.
   - ○ B. Union troops would be defeated and the war would end.
   - ○ C. Confederate troops would cut off Union access to the Potomac.
   - ○ D. Seeing their land being destroyed by war would discourage the Union.

8. Which of these was the **greatest** cause of death in the Civil War?
   - ○ A. wounds
   - ○ B. disease
   - ○ C. frostbite
   - ○ D. starvation

9. Lincoln's Emancipation Proclamation declared that

○ A. slaves in U.S. territories were free.
○ B. slaves throughout the world were free.
○ C. slaves in Confederate states were free.
○ D. slaves in Union slave states were free.

10. Women supported the Civil War cause in all of the following ways **except**

○ A. spying on the enemy.
○ B. working in factories.
○ C. fighting on the battlefield.
○ D. treating wounded soldiers.

11. Why was the Battle of Gettysburg a turning point in the war?

○ A. Lee succeeded in capturing a city in the North.
○ B. The South suffered many losses while the North had few.
○ C. The loss of troops convinced Lee to never again invade the North.
○ D. The outcome convinced European nations to aid the Confederacy.

12. Which document did Lincoln reference in his Gettysburg Address?

○ A. U.S. Constitution
○ B. Emancipation Proclamation
○ C. Preamble to the Constitution
○ D. Declaration of Independence

13. What was the result of the Battle of Vicksburg?

○ A. The Confederate troops deserted.
○ B. The Union controlled all Southern ports.
○ C. The Union gained control of the Mississippi River.
○ D. The Confederacy enlisted more troops than ever before.

14. Which of these was a danger for African American troops who fought for the Union?

○ A. If captured, they could be sold into slavery.
○ B. They were frequently attacked by other Union soldiers.
○ C. If captured, they would be forced to fight for the Confederacy.
○ D. They were easily overcome since they had no weapons.

15. Which of these describes General Sherman's march through Georgia?

○ A. an example of total war
○ B. a defeat for both armies
○ C. a peaceful end to the conflict
○ D. the bloodiest battle of the war

16. Which of these describes Grant's terms of surrender at Appomattox Court House?

○ A. They were meant to punish the Confederacy.
○ B. They were generous so as to avoid further suffering.
○ C. They were stern in their demand for payment of losses.
○ D. They were meant to show that the North sought forgiveness.

Applying Social Studies Skills

Use the table and your knowledge of history to answer the questions.

Approximate Resources in 1860 as a Percentage of the U.S. Total

Resource	North	South
Population	71%	29% (one-third slaves)
Land area	75%	25%
Farmland	65%	35%
Cotton production	4%	96%
Factories	85%	15%
Miles of railroad track	70%	30%
Iron and steel production	93%	7%
Value of exports	44%	56%
Bank deposits	81%	19%

17. How might the distribution of farmland have affected the outcome of the Civil War?

18. Based on the table, why might the North have been better equipped than the South to fight a long war?

19. Based on the table, which of the following accounted for the high value of exports in the South?
   - ○ A. banking
   - ○ B. railroads
   - ○ C. cotton production
   - ○ D. iron and steel production

Exploring the Essential Question

What factors and events influenced the outcome of the Civil War?

Follow the directions to complete the item below.

20. Write two short letters that reflect what you have learned about how the Civil War affected the lives of civilians and soldiers. Write one letter from a Union or Confederate soldier to a civilian family member. Write the other letter from a civilian family member in the North or the South to a soldier.

    In each letter, include at least three details that indicate what life was like for each letter writer. Also convey your ideas clearly, using standard English.

Creating an Act-It-Out for *The First Vote*

Your group will bring to life one image from Reconstruction. Your teacher will select one member of your group to play the part of your assigned character. A reporter will then interview characters.

Step 1: Circle the character your group is assigned.

Poll Worker (white man)

Skilled Craftsman (black man)

City Dweller (black man)

Union Army Veteran (black man)

Southern Democrat (not pictured)

Step 2: Discuss these questions. Make sure everyone in your group is prepared to answer them.

- Who are you?
- What are you doing here today?
- How do you feel about the expansion of voting rights to all black men?
- How do you feel about your future here in the South?
- Do you think Reconstruction will bring African Americans closer to full citizenship? Why or why not?

Step 3: Discuss how the person who is chosen to perform can make the character come alive through facial expressions, tone of voice, and posture. Use information from your Reading Notes, your book, and the image to make your character realistic. Collect simple props to use during the act-it-out.

Chapter 23 Assessment

Mastering the Content

Fill in the circle next to the best answer.

1. Which describes Abraham Lincoln's approach to the South at the end of the Civil War?
   - ○ A. The South should be punished for its part in the war.
   - ○ B. The South should be treated with kindness and justice.
   - ○ C. The South should ratify the Fourteenth Amendment.
   - ○ D. The South should pay for property damage caused by the war.

2. All of these were included in President Johnson's Reconstruction plan **except**
   - ○ A. cancellation of war debts.
   - ○ B. new state constitutions for Confederate states.
   - ○ C. ratification of the Thirteenth Amendment.
   - ○ D. guarantee of voting rights for freedmen.

3. Which of these was a lasting effect of the Freedmen's Bureau?
   - ○ A. job security
   - ○ B. land distribution
   - ○ C. free medical care
   - ○ D. educational opportunity

4. What was the purpose of the black codes?
   - ○ A. to control former slaves
   - ○ B. to provide fair wages for freedmen
   - ○ C. to reconstruct the plantation system
   - ○ D. to teach language skills to freedmen

5. Why was the Thirteenth Amendment passed?
   - ○ A. to abolish slavery
   - ○ B. to provide citizenship to former slaves
   - ○ C. to allow freedmen to run for office
   - ○ D. to legislate fair treatment of all citizens

6. What did Congress hope the Enforcement Acts would prevent?
   - ○ A. misuse of tax money
   - ○ B. attacks on political leaders
   - ○ C. attempts to keep people from voting
   - ○ D. opposition to new state governments

7. What does the Fourteenth Amendment guarantee to citizens?
   - ○ A. the right to vote
   - ○ B. the right to medical care
   - ○ C. equal protection of the law
   - ○ D. separate but equal public facilities

8. During Congressional Reconstruction, which group held political power in the South?
   - ○ A. wealthy, white landowners
   - ○ B. former Confederate leaders
   - ○ C. members of the Ku Klux Klan
   - ○ D. people who had been loyal to the United States

9. In 1867, which of these made up the largest group of new Southern voters?
    ○ A. African Americans
    ○ B. white Southern Democrats
    ○ C. former Confederate soldiers
    ○ D. Northerners who moved to the South

10. What was the purpose of the Fifteenth Amendment?
    ○ A. to give all citizens the right to vote
    ○ B. to provide education for all citizens
    ○ C. to raise taxes to repair damage to the South
    ○ D. to protect the voting rights of African American men

11. Why was the Ku Klux Klan formed?
    ○ A. to integrate Southern schools
    ○ B. to end government corruption
    ○ C. to return white Democrats to power
    ○ D. to protect the voting rights of Southerners

12. Why did Southern Democrats pass Jim Crow laws?
    ○ A. to assure equal education for all
    ○ B. to encourage Southerners to move to the North
    ○ C. to separate African Americans and whites in public life
    ○ D. to prevent unqualified African Americans from voting

13. How did the Supreme Court rule in *Plessy v. Ferguson*?
    ○ A. Jim Crow laws are unconstitutional.
    ○ B. Public facilities should be available to all races.
    ○ C. Integration of schools is required by law.
    ○ D. Separate but equal public facilities are constitutional.

14. What was an effect of Southern poll tax laws?
    ○ A. African Americans were denied voting rights.
    ○ B. Money was raised to fund public education.
    ○ C. Public funding of small businesses increased.
    ○ D. Southern Democrats were voted out of office.

15. Southern segregation pushed African Americans to move. What pulled them to other parts of the country?
    ○ A. the promise of free land
    ○ B. the promise of free education
    ○ C. the hope of better opportunities
    ○ D. the hope of political opportunities

16. How did African Americans who remained in the South improve their lives?
    ○ A. They depended upon government welfare.
    ○ B. They worked together to build communities.
    ○ C. They received money from relatives in the North.
    ○ D. They conducted violent protests to obtain rights.

Applying Social Studies Skills

Use the map and your knowledge of history to answer the questions.

Military Reconstruction Districts, 1870

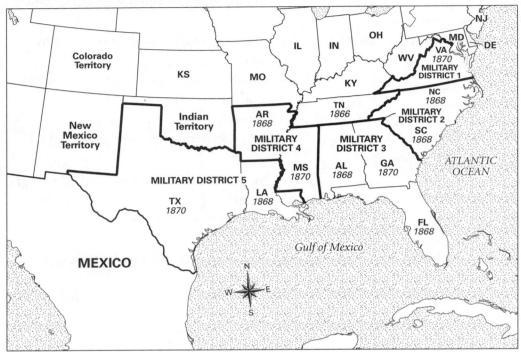

17. What do the years under the Southern states represent?

18. Why did Congress believe it was necessary to establish these military districts?
- ○ A. to provide work for soldiers
- ○ B. to quell violent slave revolts
- ○ C. to prevent another civil war
- ○ D. to form legal state governments

19. The Military Reconstruction Act was enacted in response to the actions of which president?
- ○ A. Ulysses S. Grant
- ○ B. Andrew Johnson
- ○ C. Abraham Lincoln
- ○ D. Rutherford B. Hayes

Name_____ Date_____

Exploring the Essential Question

To what extent did Reconstruction bring African Americans closer to full citizenship?

Follow the directions to complete the item below.

20. In a short essay, describe at least three ways the government tried to guarantee African Americans full citizenship during Reconstruction. Then describe three ways that various groups tried to deny African Americans full citizenship during and immediately after Reconstruction.

Make sure to convey your ideas clearly, using standard English.

Unit 7 Timeline Challenge Cards

Missouri Compromise
1820

Congress defines where slavery is permitted in the territories west of the Mississippi River. By making this compromise, Missouri is admitted to the Union as a slave state.

Compromise of 1850
1850

When California applies for statehood as a free state, some Southerners threaten to secede. Congress resolves the crisis by redefining where slavery is permitted in the territories and enacting a stronger fugitive slave law.

Kansas-Nebraska Act
1854

This acts opens up the Great Plains to settlement and nullifies the Missouri Compromise by allowing the territory to choose whether to allow slavery. Eventually, it results in violence throughout Kansas as antislavery and proslavery settlers battle for control of the territory.

Dred Scott Decision
1857

After Dred Scott, a slave, sues for his freedom, the Supreme Court declares that blacks have no rights as citizens and that Congress cannot make laws concerning slavery in the territories.

Lincoln Becomes President
1860

Abraham Lincoln is elected president of the United States, prompting 11 states to secede from the Union.

The Civil War
1861–1865

A Southern attack on Fort Sumter ignites the Civil War. Major battles in such places as Antietam and Vicksburg bring the death toll to over 620,000 by the war's end.

Emancipation Proclamation
1863

President Lincoln's Emancipation Proclamation frees the slaves in the Confederate states.

Gettysburg
1863

The last Confederate invasion of the North results in a major battle and a Southern defeat near Gettysburg, Pennsylvania. Four months later, President Lincoln travels to the site and gives the Gettysburg Address, encouraging Americans to stay strong in the fight to preserve the Union and the principles of the Declaration of Independence.

The Confederacy Surrenders
1865

General Lee and his Confederate forces surrender to General Grant at Appomattox Court House, Virginia, bringing an end to the Civil War.

Thirteenth Amendment
1865

FREE!

The Thirteenth Amendment is ratified. It outlaws slavery in the United States.

Fourteenth Amendment
1868

The Fourteenth Amendment is ratified, granting citizenship and equal civil and legal rights to African Americans and former slaves.

Fifteenth Amendment
1870

The ratification of the Fifteenth Amendment ensures that no citizen will be denied the right to vote based on race, color, or previous enslavement.

Creating a Music Video

Your group will create a one-minute music video for one of the verses of "The Heart of the Appaloosa." Each group member will help plan the video and find or create costumes and props. Have your teacher initial each step as you complete it.

_____ **Step 1: Review the roles.** Make sure everyone understands his or her role.

Music Historian: You will lead the group during Step 2 to learn about the meaning of the lyrics and in Step 6 to prepare for the "Behind the Music Video" interview.

Choreographer: You will lead the group during Step 3 to coordinate a pantomime to the song.

Special Effects Director: You will lead the group during Step 4 to prepare costumes and props.

Producer: You will lead the group during Step 5 to rehearse the music video.

_____ **Step 2: Learn about your verse.** Take turns reading aloud your verse and the background information on the handout for your verse. When you have finished, the Music Historian should record at least five main points about your verse.

_____ **Step 3: Brainstorm how performers will pantomime the lyrics.** Your video will use pantomime (storytelling with gestures and movement instead of words). The Choreographer should draw a series of sketches showing the performers' actions.

_____ **Step 4: Prepare materials.** Performers should wear simple costumes such as hats, scarves, or beads. You should also collect or create simple props to further bring the lyrics alive. The Special Effects Director should make a list of what each performer will wear and any props that will be used.

_____ **Step 5: Rehearse.** Rehearse the performance with your costumes and props. Make sure you can present the video in one minute. The Producer should make sure that each group member is actively involved, the pantomime flows smoothly, and costumes and props are used effectively.

_____ **Step 6: Prepare for your "Behind the Music Video" interview.** Assign each group member two lines of the verse. Group members should be prepared to explain what their lines mean and to point out any historical references to people or places. In addition, the Music Historian should make sure everyone in the group is able to answer these questions:

• How did it feel to perform in this music video?

• Why did you choose these props and costumes?

• What emotions do the Nez Perce experience in this verse?

• How do you think western settlement affected the Nez Perce?

Background Information on "The Heart of the Appaloosa"

"The Heart of the Appaloosa," Verse 1

From the land of shooting waters to the peaks of the Coeur d'Alene
Thimbleberries in the forest, elk grazing on the plain
The People of the Coyote made their camp along the streams
Of the green Wallowa Valley when fences had no name
And they bred a strain of horses, the treasure of the tribe
Who could toe-dance on a ridge or gallop up a mountainside
Who could haul the hunter's burden, turn a buffalo stampede
The horse that wore the spotted coat was born with matchless speed

Chorus

Thunder Rolling in the Mountains
Lead the people across the Great Divide
There's blood on the snow in the hills of Idaho
But the heart of the Appaloosa never died

Background Information for Verse 1

For thousands of years, the Nez Perce lived on the Columbia Plateau, a beautiful area of winding rivers, deep canyons, and snowcapped peaks. Elk and deer grazed in the forest, and salmon filled the streams. The Nez Perce believed that Coyote, the bravest of all animals, had placed them in this valley. According to legend, a terrible monster had once roamed the Earth. Coyote knew he must kill the monster if the world were to survive. Coyote killed the monster and created people from its flesh. He sent the people to live on the plains, in the mountains, and in the desert. He used the monster's blood to make the Nez Perce, whom he placed in the Wallowa Valley, the world's most beautiful spot.

The Nez Perce believed the land was part of the Earth Mother and should be shared by all. No one could claim the land as personal property.

One day, some spotted horses wandered into the valley. The Nez Perce bred only the healthiest and strongest of these horses, and soon they had a very sturdy breed—the magnificent Appaloosa. The Appaloosa allowed the Nez Perce to journey onto the plains. There they could hunt buffalo for food, shelter, and clothing.

"The Heart of the Appaloosa," Verse 2

In the winter came the crowned ones near frozen in the cold
Bringing firearms and spyglasses and a book that saves the soul
The people gave them welcome, nursed them till their strength returned
And studied the talking paper, its mysteries to learn
In the shadow of the mission sprang up farms and squatter towns
The plain was lined with fences, the plow blade split the ground
In the shallows of the Clearwater gold glittered in the pan
And word would come from Washington: Remove the Indian

Chorus

Thunder Rolling in the Mountains
Lead the people across the Great Divide
There's blood on the snow in the hills of Idaho
But the heart of the Appaloosa never died

Background Information for Verse 2

In 1805, members of the Lewis and Clark expedition came to the Columbia Plateau. The Nez Perce called them "the crowned ones" because they wore high hats made of beaver pelts that looked like the crowns of kings. The explorers were tired, hungry, and sick, and the Nez Perce gave them food and shelter. In return, the white men introduced the Nez Perce to guns, glass, and cloth. They also showed them the Christian Bible, which the Nez Perce called "talking paper."

Soon after, missionaries began to venture west to teach the Nez Perce to read and write and to convert them to Christianity. The missionaries and others who followed wanted to farm the rich soil of the Wallowa Valley. The Nez Perce, however, believed that digging up the land was wrong. The whites began to farm the land anyway.

In 1860, miners discovered gold in the Wallowa Valley. Soon, many miners and settlers swarmed over the Nez Perce land. The U.S. government made treaties with the Nez Perce, and some Nez Perce bands agreed to move to the Lapwai Reservation in Idaho. Other bands refused to sign any treaty.

"The Heart of the Appaloosa," Verse 3

The chief spoke to the people in his anger and his pain
"I am no more Chief Joseph, Rolling Thunder is my name
They condemn us to a wasteland of barren soil and stone
We shall fight them if we must but we will find another home"
They fled into the Bitterroot, an army at their heels
They fought at White Bird Canyon, they fought at Misery Hill
Till the colonel saw his strategy and sent the order down
To kill the Appaloosa wherever it be found

Chorus

Thunder Rolling in the Mountains
Lead the people across the Great Divide
There's blood on the snow in the hills of Idaho
But the heart of the Appaloosa never died

Background Information for Verse 3

Chief Joseph, whose Indian name means "Thunder Rolling in the Mountains,"
was the leader of the Nez Perce in the Wallowa Valley. He was very angry with the
white settlers for taking land from his people. He knew, however, that if he did
not lead his people to the Lapwai Reservation, the settlers would force them from
the land, and many of his people would be killed. On their way to the reservation,
some Indian warriors came upon settlers who had killed one of their fathers and
had beaten their friends. In revenge, the warriors killed some of these settlers.

The Nez Perce leaders knew the U.S. government would send troops to punish
them for what had happened. However, they hoped they could make peace. The
chiefs decided to move to White Bird Canyon, where they could defend themselves
if peace talks failed. But talks never began. Shots rang out as soon as the army
arrived, and both soldiers and Nez Perce died. Chief Joseph knew that his people
would be safe now only if they made their way to Canada.

After an exhausting two-month journey through mountains, canyons, and val-
leys, the Nez Perce decided to rest in eastern Montana. They mistakenly believed
that they were several days ahead of the pursuing U.S. Army. Actually, the troops
were a short distance away. In early morning, as the Indians slept, soldiers charged
into the camp and began shooting everyone they saw. The Nez Perce fought back
bravely, eventually driving the troops from the camp. After a day's fighting, 89 Nez
Perce lay dead, most of them women and children. Many of their horses were also
killed. The survivors buried their dead and resumed their flight to Canada.

"The Heart of the Appaloosa," Verse 4

Twelve hundred miles retreating, three times over the Divide
The horse their only safety, their only ally
Three thousand Appaloosas perished with the tribe
The people and the horses dying side by side
Thunder Rolling in the Mountains said, "My heart is sick and sad
The children now are freezing, the old chiefs are dead
The hunger takes our spirit, our wounds are deep and sore
From where the sun now stands I will fight no more"

Chorus

Thunder Rolling in the Mountains
Lead the people across the Great Divide
There's blood on the snow in the hills of Idaho
But the heart of the Appaloosa never died

Background Information for Verse 4

For almost four months, the men, women, and children of the Nez Perce traveled more than 1,000 miles with the white soldiers in pursuit. Along the way, 250 Nez Perce warriors fought 13 battles against 2,000 U.S. soldiers and volunteers.

When the Nez Perce were only 40 miles from the Canadian border, they decided to stop for a few days. They were hungry, tired, and cold. While they rested, the U.S. Army raced toward their camp. On a cold, rainy day, the soldiers attacked. The Nez Perce fought back, and even women and children attacked the troops with knives and digging sticks. The soldiers retreated and surrounded the camp, hoping to starve the Nez Perce into surrendering.

Chief Joseph knew that he must end his people's suffering. Early one morning, he rode his Appaloosa to the white man's camp. He handed over his rifle and surrendered. "I am tired of fighting," he said. "Our chiefs are killed . . . It is cold and we have no blankets. The little children are freezing to death. My people, some of them, have run away to the hills, and have no blankets, no food . . . My heart is sick and sad. From where the sun now stands, I will fight no more forever." He made only one request: that he and his people be allowed to return to the reservation nearest their land, in Idaho.

"The Heart of the Appaloosa," Verse 5

They were sent to Oklahoma, malaria ran rife
But more died of broken hearts far from the land that gave them life
And the man once called Joseph at death was heard to say
"We have given up our horses, they have gone away"
But sometimes without warning from a dull domestic herd
A spotted horse of spirit wondrous will emerge
Strong it is and fearless and nimble on a hill
Listening for thunder, the Appaloosa's living still

Chorus

Thunder Rolling in the Mountains
Lead the people across the Great Divide
There's blood on the snow in the hills of Idaho
But the heart of the Appaloosa never died

Background Information for Verse 5

Chief Joseph believed that he and his people would be sent back to Idaho. Instead, the government moved them to a reservation in Kansas, where they were held as prisoners. There, the Nez Perce lived under terrible conditions, suffering from malaria and despair. Twenty-one Indians died during their eight-month stay.

The soldiers then moved the Indians to a reservation in Oklahoma. The federal agent in charge of the reservation had received no food, clothing, or medicine for them. More Nez Perce died from disease, exposure, and malnutrition. They called Oklahoma the "Hot Place." Eventually, some of the Nez Perce were allowed to return to the Lapwai Reservation in Idaho. Chief Joseph was not. He and several others were sent to the Colville Reservation in Washington, where he died in 1904.

Today, some of the Nez Perce remain on land in Idaho and Washington. Many have left the reservations to live and work all over the United States. Those remaining on reservations run businesses in retail, timber, and limestone industries. Others work on the reservations' horse ranches, where they breed and raise their beloved Appaloosa.

Chapter 24 Assessment

Mastering the Content
Fill in the circle next to the best answer.

1. Which group would disagree with this statement?

   > Owning a plot of land provides a sense of freedom.

   ○ A. Texas ranchers
   ○ B. European settlers
   ○ C. U.S. government
   ○ D. American Indians

2. All of these were an effect of the Homestead Act **except**

   ○ A. an increase in U.S. farms.
   ○ B. an increase in railway lines.
   ○ C. a decrease in settlers moving west.
   ○ D. a decrease in American Indian land.

3. Which of these contributed to the flood of new settlers in the West?

   ○ A. wars in Europe
   ○ B. jobs in factories
   ○ C. growth of railroads
   ○ D. fear of American Indians

4. Which group was **most** responsible for the completion of the transcontinental railroad?

   ○ A. Great Plains homesteaders
   ○ B. Chinese immigrants
   ○ C. California miners
   ○ D. U.S. military

5. How did the U.S. government entice railroad companies to take on the transcontinental railroad project?

   ○ A. by paying for all supplies
   ○ B. by offering land subsidies
   ○ C. by providing all the laborers
   ○ D. by transporting supplies by rail

6. Which group was negatively affected by the transcontinental railroad?

   ○ A. Plains Indians
   ○ B. cattle ranchers
   ○ C. Irish immigrants
   ○ D. shipping workers

7. How did mining change the West?

   ○ A. by improving the landscape
   ○ B. by establishing law and order
   ○ C. by ending American Indian conflicts
   ○ D. by opening up areas to new settlement

8. What caused the Plains people to finally move to reservations?

   ○ A. financial incentives
   ○ B. opportunity to own land
   ○ C. educational opportunities
   ○ D. extermination of the buffalo

9. Which of these describes the long drive?
   - ○ A. the movement of cattle to railroad lines
   - ○ B. the path leading the Nez Perce to Canada
   - ○ C. the action of nailing spikes into railway ties
   - ○ D. the path followed by buffalo hunters in the Great Plains

10. Which of the following was typically the last step in this sequence?

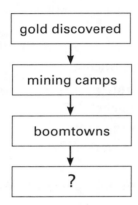

```
gold discovered
      ↓
  mining camps
      ↓
   boomtowns
      ↓
      ?
```

   - ○ A. gold rush
   - ○ B. ghost towns
   - ○ C. crime waves
   - ○ D. law and order

11. Which of these was a challenge for farmers on the Great Plains?
   - ○ A. unreliable rainfall
   - ○ B. conflicts with ranchers
   - ○ C. miners intruding on land
   - ○ D. clearing of abundant trees

12. Which material was used to build homes on the Great Plains?
   - ○ A. sod
   - ○ B. wood
   - ○ C. bricks
   - ○ D. adobe

13. Under the Indian Removal Act of 1830, what was promised to American Indians?
   - ○ A. land in the Great Plains
   - ○ B. protection of homelands
   - ○ C. land to freely hunt buffalo
   - ○ D. homes on reservations in the East

14. Which of these changed federal policy toward American Indians?
   - ○ A. destruction of the buffalo
   - ○ B. development of the West
   - ○ C. popular belief that they had been mistreated
   - ○ D. political pressure to allow them to move to reservations

15. After a successful 20 years, what caused the end of the long drive?
   - ○ A. growth of cities
   - ○ B. weather conditions
   - ○ C. conflict with farmers
   - ○ D. government regulations

16. What is the significance of the Battle of the Little Big Horn?
   - ○ A. It was a famous U.S. Army victory.
   - ○ B. It was an event that forced Congress to honor treaties.
   - ○ C. It was the last big battle between the army and American Indians.
   - ○ D. It was the longest battle fought by the army and American Indians.

Applying Social Studies Skills

Use the maps and your knowledge of history to answer the questions.

Land Losses of American Indians, 1850–2010

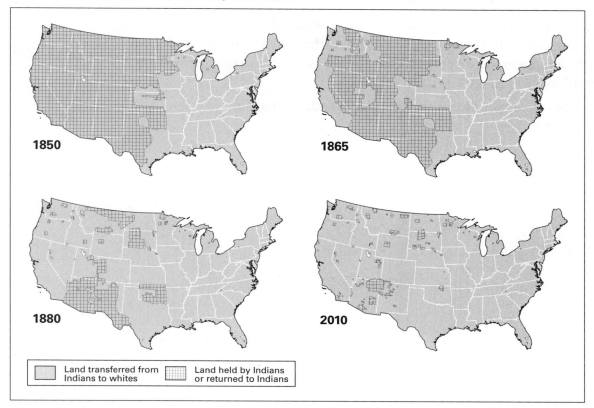

17. Based on the information in the maps, which of these statements is true?

   ○ A. American Indians immigrated to other countries.
   ○ B. At one time, American Indians moved to the East Coast.
   ○ C. American Indians lost land only in the western United States.
   ○ D. At one time, American Indians lived throughout the United States.

18. When did the largest American Indian land losses occur?

   ○ A. before 1850
   ○ B. between 1865 and 1880
   ○ C. between 1880 and 2010
   ○ D. after 2010

19. How did the United States enforce the transfer of land from American Indians to whites?

Exploring the Essential Question

How did settlers change the West and affect American Indians?

Follow the directions to complete the item below.

20. Write a short essay describing two events or policies that increased settlement in the West after the Civil War. Describe how the settlers who responded to each of these events or policies changed the West. Also explain how each event or policy affected American Indians.

    Be sure to convey your ideas clearly, using standard English.

Assignments for Making a Shirtwaist Blouse

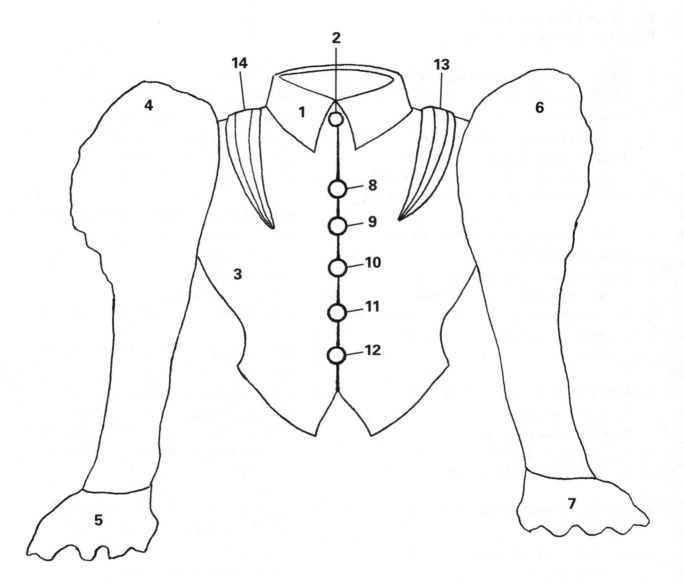

Worker 1: Collar

Worker 2: Button 1

Worker 3: Outline of body of blouse

Worker 4: Left sleeve

Worker 5: Left cuff

Worker 6: Right sleeve

Worker 7: Right cuff

Worker 8: Button 2

Worker 9: Button 3

Worker 10: Button 4

Worker 11: Button 5

Worker 12: Button 6

Worker 13: Pleat on right side

Worker 14: Pleat on left side

Chapter 25 Assessment

Mastering the Content

Fill in the circle next to the best answer.

1. What was an effect of the high tariffs that Congress placed on imported goods after the Civil War?
    ○ A. Foreign competition decreased.
    ○ B. The quality of products improved.
    ○ C. The cost of domestic goods increased.
    ○ D. New business growth was discouraged.

2. Which of these describes the economic policy known as laissez-faire?
    ○ A. government control of business
    ○ B. government protection of workers
    ○ C. government guidance of labor practices
    ○ D. government non-interference with business

3. Which of these is an entrepreneur?
    ○ A. a farm employee
    ○ B. a city factory worker
    ○ C. a government employee
    ○ D. a successful business owner

4. How were farms affected by the growth of big business?
    ○ A. Farms were bought up by factory developers.
    ○ B. New machinery provided farms a greater crop yield.
    ○ C. New machinery was too expensive for commercial farms.
    ○ D. Farms were sold because food products were imported.

5. Which of these is an important aspect of industrialization?
    ○ A. government-owned businesses
    ○ B. privately owned businesses
    ○ C. machine-made products
    ○ D. handmade goods

6. Who was responsible for developing the U.S. steel industry?
    ○ A. Max Blanck
    ○ B. Andrew Carnegie
    ○ C. John D. Rockefeller
    ○ D. Cornelius Vanderbilt

7. How did Thomas Edison improve the quality of life in U.S. cities?
    ○ A. by building tenement houses
    ○ B. by improving factory conditions
    ○ C. by inventing communication systems
    ○ D. by creating an electrical distribution system

8. Mass production of goods affected life in the United States in all of these ways **except**
    ○ A. more factories were built.
    ○ B. more people were employed.
    ○ C. products were more affordable.
    ○ D. working conditions were better.

9. What was one purpose of the business organization known as the trust?

○ A. to control prices
○ B. to reward employees
○ C. to offer quality training
○ D. to provide employee benefits

10. John D. Rockefeller was a giant in which industry?

○ A. oil
○ B. steel
○ C. tobacco
○ D. railroads

11. How did monopolies threaten the free-enterprise system?

○ A. by reducing prices
○ B. by increasing foreign trade
○ C. by eliminating competition
○ D. by encouraging labor disputes

12. Which of these was an effect of the rapid growth of cities due to industrialization?

○ A. crowded tenement housing
○ B. immigration restrictions
○ C. improved city services
○ D. high unemployment

13. Who led the labor group called the American Federation of Labor?

○ A. Max Blanck
○ B. Leland Stanford
○ C. Samuel Gompers
○ D. William Vanderbilt

14. What was the outcome of the Homestead Strike?

○ A. Strikers convinced the owner of the plant to raise their pay and improve their working conditions.
○ B. Strikers got better working conditions but no raise in pay.
○ C. The union collapsed in defeat.
○ D. The union became stronger.

15. Labor unions were organized to represent the interests of

○ A. workers.
○ B. consumers.
○ C. corporations.
○ D. entrepreneurs.

16. Which of these would have prevented the 1911 tragedy at the Triangle Factory in New York?

○ A. hiring more seamstresses
○ B. buying up-to-date equipment
○ C. keeping factory doors unlocked
○ D. allowing people to join labor unions

Applying Social Studies Skills

This political cartoon shows senators in the Senate chamber. The figures in the back symbolize business trusts. Use the cartoon and your knowledge of history to answer the questions.

17. What does the cartoonist think of business trusts?

○ A. They are too powerful.
○ B. They provide political guidance.
○ C. They are a necessary part of the political process.
○ D. They provide financial support for government programs.

18. What effect did trusts have on the political process?

○ A. They insured that laws were fair and just.
○ B. They used their wealth to influence election results.
○ C. They used their power to establish strict labor laws.
○ D. They insured that bills were proposed to control business.

19. What techniques does the cartoonist use to convey his message?

Exploring the Essential Question

Did the benefits of industrialization outweigh the costs?

Follow the directions to complete the item below.

20. Write a four-paragraph essay that responds to these four questions:
    - In the late 19th century, what conditions allowed for the growth of industry in the United States?
    - How did industrialization improve life in the United States?
    - How did industrialization hurt life in the United States?
    - Did the benefits of industrialization outweigh the costs? Support your opinion with facts.

    Be sure to convey your ideas clearly, using standard English.

Creating an Immigrant Scrapbook

You and your partner will create a scrapbook highlighting what life was like for a U.S. immigrant in the early 1900s. The scrapbook will contain biographical information, notes about the journey from the home country, and descriptions of life in the United States.

Your scrapbook must be free of grammatical errors and have these four elements.

Element 1 An introductory page with background information on your immigrant. This page should include

- a fictitious name, date of birth, and native country.
- a description of the immigrant's family.
- an explanation of the events or circumstances that prompted this person to leave his or her country.
- at least one visual, such as a simple sketch or a historical photograph. Each visual must have a short caption.

Element 2 One page about the journey to the United States. This page should include

- at least one written document, such as a letter from a family member in the United States or an entry from the immigrant's personal journal.
- at least one artifact the immigrant used on the journey, such as a passport, a ticket, or coins from the home country. Each artifact must have a short caption that explains what it is and how it was used.
- at least one visual that shows something that happened on the journey. Each visual must have a short caption.

Element 3 One page about the immigrant's experiences upon arrival in the United States. This page should include

- at least one written document, such as a letter the immigrant wrote to family or friends in the home country or an entry from the immigrant's personal journal.
- at least one artifact the immigrant used upon arrival, such as a paycheck or a page from an English dictionary. Each artifact must have a short caption that explains what it is and how it was used.
- at least one visual that represents the immigrant's new life in the United States. Each visual must have a short caption.

Element 4 Creative touches that make your scrapbook look authentic.

Chapter 26 Assessment

Mastering the Content

Fill in the circle next to the best answer.

1. What did the United States offer immigrants that they could not get in their homeland?
   - ○ A. clean cities
   - ○ B. plentiful jobs
   - ○ C. close families
   - ○ D. home ownership

2. What did assimilation require of immigrants?
   - ○ A. working on farms
   - ○ B. purchasing businesses
   - ○ C. changing religious beliefs
   - ○ D. adapting to a new way of life

3. Between 1880 and 1920, Europeans' introduction to the United States was at
   - ○ A. Ellis Island.
   - ○ B. Angel Island.
   - ○ C. Los Angeles Airport.
   - ○ D. Grand Central Station.

4. Why were U.S. immigrants often met with resentment?
   - ○ A. People thought they took jobs away from citizens.
   - ○ B. People were envious of their wealth and experience.
   - ○ C. People thought the country would become too crowded.
   - ○ D. People were afraid they would take over the country.

5. Why did many Jews emigrate from eastern Europe?
   - ○ A. to escape poverty
   - ○ B. to attend universities
   - ○ C. to become entrepreneurs
   - ○ D. to escape religious persecution

6. Which of these would prevent an immigrant from entering the United States?
   - ○ A. inability to speak English
   - ○ B. failure to pass a health exam
   - ○ C. inability to pay the entrance fee
   - ○ D. failure to have a permanent job

7. Which of these is true about **most** immigrants to the United States?
   - ○ A. They fit in very easily.
   - ○ B. They helped build the economy.
   - ○ C. They offered their skills but demanded high wages.
   - ○ D. They earned a lot of money and returned to their homelands.

8. Compared to earlier immigrants, which of these describes those who arrived between 1880 and 1920?
   - ○ A. They were wealthier.
   - ○ B. They all spoke English.
   - ○ C. They were more diverse.
   - ○ D. They were better educated.

9. Why did immigrants form ethnic neighborhoods?
   - ○ A. They wanted better housing.
   - ○ B. They were not accepted elsewhere.
   - ○ C. They did not want to live with citizens.
   - ○ D. They did not want to share their culture.

10. Which of these was a result of immigration in the United States?
    - ○ A. cultural diversity
    - ○ B. religious freedom
    - ○ C. high-rise buildings
    - ○ D. public school systems

11. How are refugees different from other immigrants?
    - ○ A. They are invited to live in a country.
    - ○ B. They are fleeing to save their lives.
    - ○ C. They are criminals banished from their country.
    - ○ D. They are people who leave their family behind.

12. Why did so many Mexicans come to the United States between 1910 and 1920?
    - ○ A. to search for gold
    - ○ B. to flee religious persecution
    - ○ C. to escape the Mexican Revolution
    - ○ D. to claim lands lost during the Mexican American War

13. Nativism is most closely related to which of these words?
    - ○ A. equality
    - ○ B. tolerance
    - ○ C. diversity
    - ○ D. prejudice

14. All of these beliefs caused the wave of nativism in the early 1900s **except**
    - ○ A. that immigrants competed for jobs.
    - ○ B. that immigrants would not work.
    - ○ C. that immigrants were criminals.
    - ○ D. that immigrants caused slums.

15. Which group of people was **most** affected by the bans on immigration passed in 1882 and 1907?
    - ○ A. Asians
    - ○ B. Germans
    - ○ C. Africans
    - ○ D. Mexicans

16. What was an effect of the quota system established by Congress in 1921?
    - ○ A. Immigration of Africans increased.
    - ○ B. Immigrants returned to their home countries.
    - ○ C. The United States had fewer immigrants than in the past.
    - ○ D. The United States refused to accept any new immigrants.

Applying Social Studies Skills

Use the map and your knowledge of history to answer the questions.

Immigration to the United States, 1820–1990

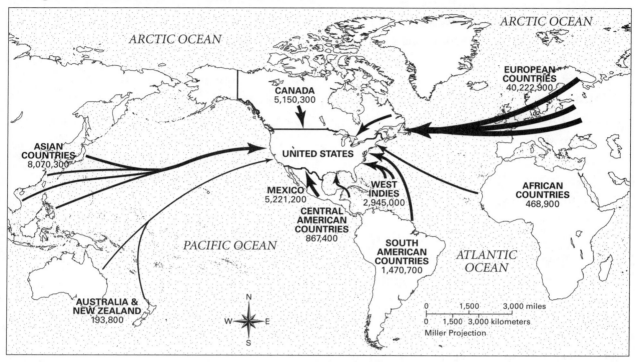

17. Why are the arrows on the map of different thicknesses?

18. Which of these questions cannot be answered by studying this map?
   - ○ A. Why did people immigrate to the United States?
   - ○ B. From which parts of the world did people emigrate?
   - ○ C. From which continent did the most people emigrate?
   - ○ D. What was the shortest route to travel to the United States?

19. Based on the map, which of these groups of immigrants traveled the farthest to reach the United States?
   - ○ A. Mexicans
   - ○ B. Canadians
   - ○ C. West Indians
   - ○ D. New Zealanders

Exploring the Essential Question

What was life like for immigrants in the early 1900s?

Follow the directions to complete the item below.

20. The poem on the Statue of Liberty's base conveyed a welcoming message to immigrants who arrived at Ellis Island in the early 1900s. But immigrants did not find life in the United States easy, and they often felt unwelcome.

    Suppose you are a teenager who entered the United States at Ellis Island in 1910. Write a letter to your cousin back home about your first year in the United States. In your letter, write about

    - the opportunities you had.
    - the challenges you faced.
    - your impressions of the United States.

    Convey your ideas clearly, using standard English.

Unit 8 Timeline Challenge Cards

Gold Rush Begins
1848

Gold is discovered in California. Miners from all over the world flock to the West in hopes of becoming rich.

Plains Indians Forced onto Reservations
1860–1890

The government relocates Plains Indians onto reservations to make room for continued settlement of the West. Some Indian groups resist and clash with government forces.

Homestead Act
1862

The Homestead Act gives 160 acres of land in the West to settlers willing to work the land.

Transcontinental Railroad Completed
1869

The Transcontinental Railroad is completed, connecting the Atlantic and Pacific coasts and opening the West to further development.

Battle of the Little Big Horn
1876

Sioux and Cheyenne Indians successfully fight off an attack by the U.S. Army in the Battle of the Little Big Horn, also known as Custer's Last Stand. All the soldiers in the battle are killed.

Invention of the Lightbulb
1879

Thomas Edison's workshop invents the first practical electric lightbulb. By the end of the 1880s, small electrical stations provide power to city blocks in a number of cities.

Immigration's High Tide
1880–1920

More than 23 million immigrants arrive in the United States. Most flock to cities, where industry is booming and jobs are plentiful.

Haymarket Square Riot
1886

Fighting erupts and several people are killed at a rally for an eight-hour workday at Haymarket Square in Chicago. It is not until 1938 that most workers win the right to an eight-hour workday.

Homestead Plant Strike
1892

Workers striking for better working conditions clash with armed guards at a Carnegie steel plant in Homestead, Pennsylvania. The plant soon reopens with strikebreakers, and the union collapses.

First Flight
1903

The Wright brothers successfully pilot the first airplane in Kitty Hawk, North Carolina. The flight spurs worldwide interest in flying.

Triangle Shirtwaist Factory Fire
1911

A fire at the Triangle Shirtwaist Factory in New York City kills 146 girls and women. The tragedy brings to light the poor working conditions in urban factories.

Immigrant Quota System
1921

Congress establishes a quota system restricting the number of immigrants allowed into the United States each year.

Biographies of Progressive Era Leaders

Andrew Carnegie, Captain of Industry

Andrew Carnegie was born to a poor family in Scotland in 1835. He moved to Pittsburgh, Pennsylvania, when he was 13. After starting work in a textile mill, he got a job as a railroad telegraph operator and rose quickly through the ranks.

Carnegie was lively, quick-witted, and interested in everything. He loved to talk and write about what he knew. When giving speeches later in his life, he tended to stand on tiptoe (to make up for his short height) and wave his arms. Shrewd investments made Carnegie wealthy, and his wealth grew even more when he decided to concentrate on steel. He soon controlled the industry.

Carnegie was a strong believer in unregulated competition and social Darwinism, the idea that competition allows the fit to succeed and the weak to remain poor. This might be harsh, Carnegie said, but overall it made society stronger. "The price which society pays for the law of competition [is] great, but the advantages of this law are also greater still, for it is to this law that we owe our wonderful . . . development."

Carnegie became one of the richest men in the world. Before he died, he gave away 90 percent of his immense wealth, mostly to organizations that would help people to improve themselves, such as libraries and universities.

- -

John D. Rockefeller, Captain of Industry

John Davison Rockefeller was born in New York State in 1839. His father was a traveling salesman, and his mother was deeply religious and moral. Rockefeller learned about business from his father and followed his mother's beliefs about hard work and giving to those in need. Even when he was young and still struggling for money, he gave 10 percent of his income to charity.

As a person, Rockefeller was cold and precise. He walked with evenly measured steps and was not very talkative, choosing his words carefully when he did speak. His daily routine included a lunch of milk and crackers, as well as a scheduled "restorative" nap. One acquaintance described him as "the most unemotional man I had ever known."

Rockefeller began his career as a bookkeeper. He then started a business handling grain, meat, and other goods, which was quickly successful. In 1863, he built an oil refinery in Cleveland, Ohio. Five years later, this refinery was the largest in the world.

Rockefeller worked to control every step of the oil industry—wells, refineries, pipes, and barrels. He believed that too much competition forced businesses to offer unprofitably low prices and poor-quality goods. "I saw a marvelous future for our country and I wanted to participate in the work of making our country great," he once said.

Theodore Roosevelt, Trust-Busting President

Theodore "Teddy" Roosevelt was born in New York City in 1858. As a child, he was weak and suffered from severe asthma and poor eyesight. He was determined, however, to improve his health. He taught himself to box, hunt, and ride horses, and he developed a lifelong love of vigorous exercise and outdoor activities. As a public figure, Roosevelt loved being the center of attention and was instantly recognizable for his small spectacles, bushy mustache, huge smile, and loud, squeaky voice.

Roosevelt graduated with honors from Harvard and eventually entered politics. He made a name for himself as a hero in the Spanish-American War. After the war, he was elected governor of New York and then vice president. In 1901, he became the youngest president in U.S. history when William McKinley was assassinated.

As president, Roosevelt was popular with the American people for his dedication to "the little guy." He supported a wide variety of progressive reforms, including government action to control and limit corporate monopolies and trusts. Roosevelt was not opposed to all large corporations. However, he stood behind the 1912 platform of the Progressive Party: "This country belongs to the people who inhabit it. Its resources, its business, its institutions and its laws should be utilized, maintained or altered in whatever manner will best promote the general interest."

- -

Robert La Follette, Fighter for Political Reform

Robert "Fighting Bob" La Follette was born to a Wisconsin pioneer family in 1855. After going to college and becoming a lawyer, he ran for county district attorney. His party leader would not support him, so La Follette went out and campaigned directly to voters. He won the election and started a lifelong struggle to take politics out of the hands of corrupt political bosses and business leaders. "The American people . . ." he said, must have "control over their government."

Though La Follette was a small, thin man, he was a powerful speaker with a thundering voice and a habit of pounding his fist into his palm to emphasize his points. In his political career, he served as a U.S. congressman and senator, as well as governor of Wisconsin, and also ran a strong race for president.

La Follette fought for a variety of Progressive reforms, including workers' rights, women's suffrage, and the breakup of monopolies. But he was best known for his reforms of the political system. He exposed politicians who offered him bribes. He fought to have political candidates selected by voters instead of party bosses. He lectured throughout the country on the importance of reform. La Follette held fierce beliefs and was unafraid to take politically unpopular positions.

Mother Jones, Champion of Workers' Rights

Born in Ireland in 1830, Mary Harris, later known as Mother Jones, moved to Canada as a child. She worked as a teacher before marrying George Jones, a laborer like her father. After her husband and all four of her children died of yellow fever, Jones moved to Chicago and worked as a dressmaker. She was struck by how her wealthy clients had no concern for the poor and homeless, who could be seen from the window of her shop.

After her business was destroyed in a fire, Jones became heavily involved with the Knights of Labor, a labor organization. She traveled throughout the country, giving speeches at strikes, demonstrations, and labor meetings. A small woman, dressed in a black bonnet and high-collared dresses, she looked matronly (motherlike) and earned the name Mother Jones.

In spite of her appearance, Jones was an impressive speaker. When especially moved, her voice became low and powerful, and she could bring her audience to tears, laughter, or rage. She organized strikes and demonstrations, often involving women and children in order to make a stronger impact. Throughout her life, Mother Jones fought for workers' rights because, as she said, "There are no limits to which the powers of privilege will not go to keep the workers in slavery."

- -

John Muir, Protector of the Environment

Born in Scotland in 1838, John Muir immigrated to Wisconsin with his family in 1849. He worked hard on his family's farm, rising every day before dawn to have time to read. Lively and engaging, Muir had intense blue eyes and, later, a long, white beard. He worked in a factory after finishing school, but an injury almost cost him his sight and convinced him to leave the mechanized world and focus on the natural world.

Muir traveled throughout many parts of the world, keeping careful notes on plants, animals, and rocks. But he fell in love with Yosemite Valley, in California, and was appalled by the way the beautiful area was being treated. Trees thousands of years old were being cut down for lumber, meadows were being stripped bare by grazing sheep, and many tourists who visited the area had no respect for the wilderness.

Muir's humor, intelligence, and passion were compelling, and he gathered support for protecting natural areas. He wrote articles, gave speeches, and took President Roosevelt camping in Yosemite to convince him, and all Americans, of the importance of wilderness conservation. "Brought into right relationships with the wilderness, man would see that his appropriation [taking] of Earth's resources beyond his personal needs," he said, "would only bring imbalance and . . . ultimate loss and poverty . . . [to] all."

W. E. B. Du Bois, Spokesperson for Equal Rights for African Americans

William Du Bois was born in Massachusetts in 1868 and grew up in a small, close-knit community. Although there was little open discrimination where he lived, he was aware at an early age of the "vast veil" of prejudice that separated blacks and whites. While at college in Tennessee, he saw the terrible poverty and lack of education from which many black communities suffered.

After studying at Harvard College and in Germany, he became a professor at Atlanta University in Georgia. Du Bois was elegant, stately, and self-assured in appearance, manner, and expression. His poise and intelligence made him a natural leader. Du Bois was active in the newly formed National Association for the Advancement of Colored People. He edited the NAACP's monthly magazine, wrote essays, and organized conferences.

This was a period when African American arts, culture, and pride were blossoming, as was the struggle for equality. But there were different views on the approaches blacks should take to gain that equality. Some leaders thought they should try to fit into white society as best they could. Du Bois disagreed. Instead, he believed that African Americans should protest strongly for equal rights and opportunities and rely on their own communities and culture to lift them up. "We must strive for the right which the world accords to men," he said.

Upton Sinclair, Muckraker for Consumers

Upton Sinclair was born in 1878 in Baltimore, Maryland. His father was ruined by drinking, and Sinclair was opposed to alcohol his whole life. When he was ten, the family moved to New York City, where he attended school for the first time. He completed all eight grades in just two years. Sinclair kept up this rapid pace, churning out a novel a week while studying at Columbia University.

Sinclair was a serious and focused person, and he dedicated his writing and his life to social reform. He was determined to turn his pen into a weapon against injustice. With his book *The Jungle,* about an immigrant working in Chicago's meatpacking industry, he wanted to reveal the terrible conditions that workers faced. The book had a much larger impact, however, in describing the horrible quality of packaged meat. As a result of the novel, the Meat Inspection Act was passed in 1906.

Sinclair accomplished what few writers are able to do—bringing about new laws and real change—but was disappointed not to have affected larger issues. "Capitalism stands for liberty of a sort—the liberty . . . to exploit . . . We are seeking to establish and to protect a new kind of liberty . . . to enjoy the fruits of one's own labor."

Alice Paul, Crusader for Women's Rights

Alice Paul was born in New Jersey in 1885. Raised a Quaker, she was strongly influenced by her upbringing, which emphasized nonviolence and the equality of all people. After college, Paul worked in London, England. There she became involved in the struggle for women's rights and learned about the importance of militant, or aggressive, nonviolent action. To achieve reforms, a friend told her, "You have to make more noise than anybody else, you have to make yourself more obtrusive [noticeable] than anybody else, you have to fill all the papers more than anybody else."

After three years in England, Paul returned to the United States and devoted herself to the struggle for women's suffrage, or right to vote. Although personally quiet and unassuming, Paul was a fierce fighter, tough enough to survive repeated jailings, hunger strikes, and force-feedings. She organized marches in Washington, D.C., as well as pickets in front of the White House that lasted for months. The angry reaction of men almost turned one of her marches into a riot.

More moderate suffrage supporters feared Paul's aggressiveness would turn people against the issue. But her efforts raised widespread publicity and considerable public sympathy. After women gained the vote in 1920, Paul spent the rest of her life fighting for many other women's rights.

Masks of Progressive Era Leaders

Andrew Carnegie

John D. Rockefeller

Theodore Roosevelt

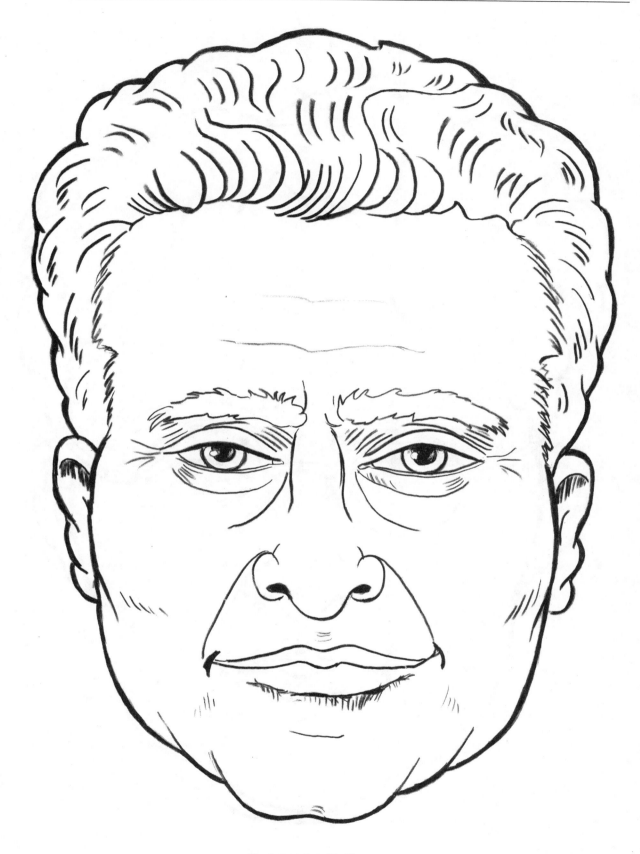

Robert La Follette

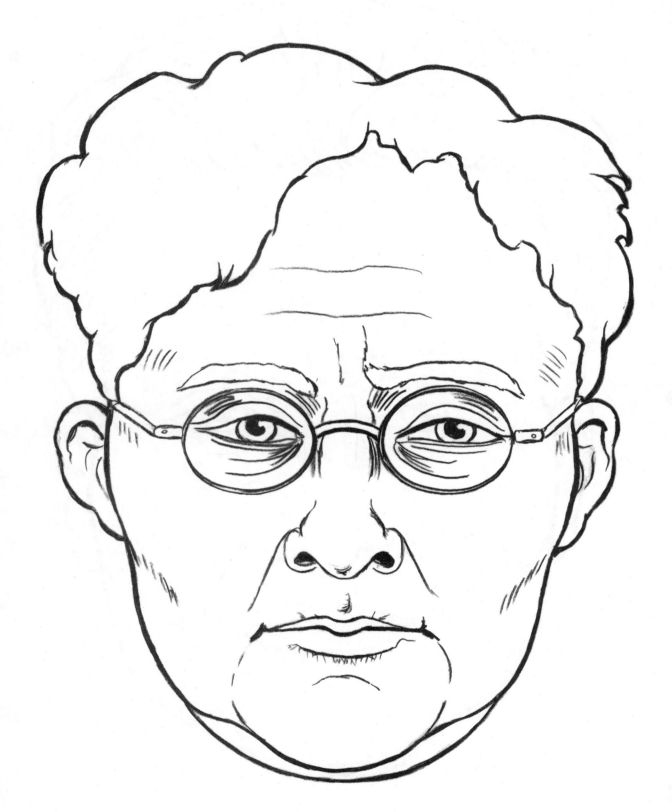

Mother Jones

John Muir

W. E. B. Du Bois

Upton Sinclair

Alice Paul

Progressive Era Panel Discussion

Round 1

Panelists: Give a 30-second to 60-second introduction of yourselves.

Audience members: Begin your Reading Notes by filling in the first column of the matrix with appropriate adjectives.

Round 2

Panelists: Discuss this question:

- Is something wrong in America?

Audience members: Begin filling in the second column of your Reading Notes matrix with answers to this question.

Round 3

Panelists: Discuss these questions:

- Have the progressives improved life in the United States?
- Have the progressives gone far enough—or too far—to improve life in the United States?

Audience members: Begin filling in the third column of your Reading Notes matrix with answers to these questions.

Round 4

Panelists: Answer questions from your fellow panelists.

Audience members: Begin filling in the fourth column of your Reading Notes matrix with questions you would like to ask.

Chapter 27 Assessment

Mastering the Content

Fill in the circle next to the best answer.

1. All of these were motivating forces for change in the Progressive era **except**
   - ○ A. racial prejudice.
   - ○ B. business monopolies.
   - ○ C. religious persecution.
   - ○ D. environmental destruction.

2. Which industry was helped by the National Grange?
   - ○ A. mining
   - ○ B. logging
   - ○ C. farming
   - ○ D. banking

3. Which of these was a particular target of the National Grange?
   - ○ A. railroad business practices
   - ○ B. African American rights
   - ○ C. women's suffrage rights
   - ○ D. child labor practices

4. How did the Populist Party impact life in the United States?
   - ○ A. It grew to be a political power.
   - ○ B. It secured the power of big business.
   - ○ C. It identified issues that needed to be addressed.
   - ○ D. It opposed change, which delayed reform measures.

5. Which of these was a benefit of big business?
   - ○ A. fair labor practices
   - ○ B. low unemployment
   - ○ C. increased leisure time
   - ○ D. safe working conditions

6. Which of these is true of John D. Rockefeller and Andrew Carnegie in their later years?
   - ○ A. They spent their wealth fighting reformers.
   - ○ B. They were elected to national political office.
   - ○ C. They used their wealth to improve the lives of many people.
   - ○ D. They prevented the government from breaking up monopolies.

7. Which of these was a goal of trust-busting?
   - ○ A. to end racial discrimination
   - ○ B. to require truth in advertising
   - ○ C. to restore business competition
   - ○ D. to reform selection of candidates

8. To what was Andrew Carnegie referring when he said these words?

   > ". . . outranks any other one thing that a community can do to benefit its people."

   - ○ A. the building of libraries
   - ○ B. the creation of highways
   - ○ C. the funding of public parks
   - ○ D. the construction of factories

9. Mary Harris Jones led the fight against
○ A. pollution.
○ B. child labor.
○ C. discrimination.
○ D. food contamination.

10. What was Upton Sinclair's primary goal in writing *The Jungle*?
○ A. to establish dietary guidelines for the public
○ B. to establish government regulation of the drug industry
○ C. to reveal racial inequality in the workplace
○ D. to reveal the terrible plight of factory workers

11. Which reform movement was the focus of the NAACP?
○ A. child labor
○ B. equal rights
○ C. humane animal treatment
○ D. environmental protection

12. John Muir and Theodore Roosevelt worked together on which reform movement?
○ A. racial equality
○ B. child labor practices
○ C. safe food and drug laws
○ D. environmental protection

13. Which of these was included on the platform of the Populist Party?
○ A. women's suffrage
○ B. a minimum wage law
○ C. national health benefits
○ D. an eight-hour workday

14. How did the direct primary increase citizen's political power?
○ A. Party candidates were chosen by party members.
○ B. Party candidates were chosen by party bosses.
○ C. Citizens voted to recall elected officials.
○ D. Citizens voted for all laws.

15. Based on information in the chapter, which pair of people had conflicting views on conditions in the United States?
○ A. Andrew Carnegie and John D. Rockefeller
○ B. Robert La Follette and Theodore Roosevelt
○ C. William McKinley and Andrew Carnegie
○ D. Theodore Roosevelt and John D. Rockefeller

16. Which of these was the result of the efforts of Alice Paul and the National Women's Party?
○ A. Women across the country voted in national elections.
○ B. Women were elected to national office for the first time.
○ C. Women were legally assured of safe working conditions.
○ D. Women received the same pay as men for comparable work.

Applying Social Studies Skills

Use the excerpt below and your knowledge of history to answer the questions.

> There was never the least attention paid to what was cut up for sausage; there would come all the way back from Europe old sausage that had been rejected, and that was moldy and white—it would be dosed with borax and glycerine, and dumped into the hoppers, and made over again for home consumption.
>
> There would be meat that had tumbled out on the floor, in the dirt and sawdust, where the workers had tramped and spit uncounted billions of consumption germs. There would be meat stored in great piles in rooms; and the water from leaky roofs would drip over it, and thousands of rats would race about on it. It was too dark in these storage places to see well, but a man could run his hand over these piles of meat and sweep off handfuls of the dried dung of rats. These rats were nuisances, and the packers would put poisoned bread out for them; they would die, and then rats, bread, and meat would go into the hoppers together.
>
> This is no fairy story and no joke . . . there were things that went into the sausage in comparison with which a poisoned rat was a tidbit.
>
> —Upton Sinclair, *The Jungle* (1906)

17. Why might the author, Upton Sinclair, be called a muckraker?
   - ○ A. He wrote about social evils.
   - ○ B. He tried to organize labor union.
   - ○ C. He twisted the truth for his own purposes.
   - ○ D. He demanded that politicians change laws.

18. Why has the author **most likely** chosen to write such vivid descriptions?
   - ○ A. to entertain the reader
   - ○ B. to embarrass the workers
   - ○ C. to win a prize for literature
   - ○ D. to create urgency for change

19. Why does the author include the phrase "This is no fairy story and no joke" in this passage?

Exploring the Essential Question

Did the progressives improve life in the United States?

Follow the directions to complete the item below.

20. Write a short essay about the United States at the beginning of the 20th century.

    - In your essay, describe one specific condition that needed to be changed.
    - Using what you learned in the chapter, be as detailed as possible in describing how Americans were negatively affected by that condition.
    - Then, describe in detail what an individual or a group did to change that condition.
    - Finally, evaluate the reform measure you described. Explain how life in the United States improved or did not improve due to the efforts of progressives.

    Be sure to convey your ideas clearly, using standard English.

Chapter 28 Assessment

Mastering the Content
Fill in the circle next to the best answer.

1. What did the United States hope to achieve through expansionism?
   - ○ A. improved foreign relations
   - ○ B. increased U.S. immigration
   - ○ C. new markets for U.S. goods
   - ○ D. exploration of unknown lands

2. How did the Hawaiian Islands become part of the United States?
   - ○ A. Hawaii was ceded by Spain.
   - ○ B. Hawaii was purchased from Japan.
   - ○ C. The United States annexed Hawaii.
   - ○ D. The Hawaiian people chose to be part of the United States.

3. How did yellow journalism contribute to U.S. involvement in Cuba's fight for independence?
   - ○ A. Exaggerated news reports created sympathy for Cuba.
   - ○ B. Sales of newspapers funded a revolution in Cuba.
   - ○ C. Writers demanded that reporters held in Cuban jails be freed.
   - ○ D. Reporters wrote accurate accounts of events occurring in Cuba.

4. The battle cry "Remember the *Maine*!" preceded which event?
   - ○ A. World War I
   - ○ B. Panama's revolution
   - ○ C. the Battle at Manila Bay
   - ○ D. the Spanish-American War

5. Why did U.S. expansionists want to annex the Philippines?
   - ○ A. It was rich in natural resources.
   - ○ B. It provided access to Chinese markets.
   - ○ C. The Filipinos wanted to become U.S. citizens.
   - ○ D. The Filipinos and Americans had similar cultures.

6. Which of these was a result of the Spanish-American War?
   - ○ A. Puerto Rico won its independence.
   - ○ B. The United States acquired Alaska.
   - ○ C. Panama broke away from Columbia.
   - ○ D. The United States annexed the Philippines.

7. Which country won independence through a peace treaty with Spain?
   - ○ A. Cuba
   - ○ B. Hawaii
   - ○ C. Panama
   - ○ D. Philippines

8. Which group gained the most from the opening of the Panama Canal in 1914?
   - ○ A. German sailors
   - ○ B. U.S. shipping lines
   - ○ C. Colombian government
   - ○ D. West Indian canal workers

9. Examine the timeline.

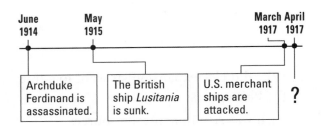

Which of these belongs in place of the question mark?

○ A. The League of Nations is formed.
○ B. The Treaty of Versailles is signed.
○ C. The United States declares war against Germany.
○ D. The Central Powers declare war against the United States.

10. Which of these words **best** describes President Woodrow Wilson before and after World War I?

○ A. imperialist
○ B. isolationist
○ C. expansionist
○ D. abolitionist

11. How did the rise of nationalism contribute to the growing unrest before the start of World War I?

○ A. Countries wanted to be rid of their foreign rulers.
○ B. Countries attempted to increase their territory.
○ C. Countries wanted to isolate themselves from other nations.
○ D. Countries wanted to form coalitions between nations.

12. How did U.S. entry into World War I affect the war?

○ A. Germany quickly surrendered.
○ B. German men enlisted in record numbers.
○ C. U.S. soldiers and equipment weakened the Germans.
○ D. Untrained U.S. forces and poor strategies lengthened the fighting.

13. Which of these contributed to the enormous loss of life during World War I?

○ A. the use of new weapons
○ B. the limited number of troops
○ C. the superiority of Germany's navy
○ D. the lack of leadership on both sides

14. All of these were included under Wilson's 14-point agreement following World War I **except**

○ A. reparations from Germany.
○ B. reduction in weapon supplies.
○ C. new boundaries for European countries.
○ D. the formation of an international association.

15. How did Germans view the Treaty of Versailles?

○ A. They felt they were treated fairly.
○ B. They were bitter about the demands.
○ C. They refused to accept the conditions of surrender.
○ D. They saw the benefit of surrendering their territory.

16. What was a contributing factor to the failure of the League of Nations?

○ A. European nations refused to join.
○ B. The United States did not participate.
○ C. Germany demanded to be represented.
○ D. The League did not have a permanent headquarters.

Name_____ Date_____

Use the political cartoon and your knowledge of history to answer the questions.

17. Why did the cartoonist choose to use a block of ice to symbolize the geographical subject of the cartoon?

18. What information changed the historical viewpoint expressed in the cartoon?
   - ○ A. the wealth of natural resources in Alaska
   - ○ B. the discovery that few people lived in Alaska
   - ○ C. the discovery of Alaska's location in the world
   - ○ D. the conditions that Russia placed on the sale of Alaska

19. What does the word *TREATY* in the cartoon refer to?
   - ○ A. the transfer of land from Russia to the United States
   - ○ B. the rules of trade between Russia and the United States
   - ○ C. the terms of peace between Russia and the United States
   - ○ D. the agreement to reduce weapon supplies in Russia and the United States

Exploring the Essential Question

Should U.S. actions in world affairs around the turn of the 20th century be praised or condemned?

Follow the directions to complete the item below.

20. Suppose you are debating U.S. actions in world affairs at the turn of the 20th century. Write a paragraph praising U.S. actions in the 20th century and, taking the other side, write a paragraph condemning U.S. actions at the turn of the 20th century. Support each viewpoint with factual information. Finally, considering the two sides of the issue, write an opinion explaining why you favor one viewpoint over the other. Be sure to convey your ideas clearly, using standard English.

How to Play *Name That Event!*

Objective

In this game, teams will guess the historical events pantomimed by other teams. Each team that makes a correct guess will be awarded 1 point. Teams will also receive 1 point for each correct guess of their own pantomime IF they can correctly explain how that event shapes our life today. The team with the most points at the end of the game wins.

Directions

Step 1: Each team draws an Event Card and secretly prepares a pantomime of that historical event. (Actors may not speak during a pantomime.) Each team also prepares a short answer to this question: *How does this event shape how we live today?*

Step 2: One team is given 1 minute to pantomime their event.

Step 3: Teams in the audience get 1 minute to guess which event from the list below was pantomimed. They write the letter of their choice and their team number on a slip of paper and hand it to the teacher.

Step 4: The presenting team answers this question: *How does this event shape how we live today?*

Step 5: The teacher tallies the points, and a new team takes a turn.

Historical Events

Event A The world's first scheduled airline service opens in Florida.

Event B The nation's first commercial radio stations begin broadcasting.

Event C The Cold War between the United States and the Soviet Union takes place.

Event D The first regularly scheduled television programs begin broadcasting.

Event E The Supreme Court ends racial segregation in schools.

Event F Martin Luther King Jr. speaks out for civil rights at the March on Washington.

Event G César Chávez organizes a nationwide boycott of table grapes.

Event H The first personal computers appear in offices.

Event I The public learns from scientists that Earth's climate is growing warmer at an alarming rate.

Event J Barack Obama becomes the first African American U.S. president.

Event Cards

1946

The first regularly scheduled television programs began broadcasting.

1963

Martin Luther King Jr. speaks out for civil rights at the March on Washington.

1968

César Chávez organizes a nationwide boycott of table grapes.

1914

The world's first scheduled airline service opens in Florida.

1988

Public learns from scientists that Earth's climate is growing warmer at an alarming rate.

1947–1991

The Cold War between the United States and the Soviet Union takes place.

1981

The first personal computers appear in offices.

2009

Barack Obama becomes the first African American U.S. president.

Chapter 29 Assessment

Mastering the Content

Fill in the circle next to the best answer.

1. How did Henry Ford make the Model T more affordable?
   ○ A. by reducing workers' wages
   ○ B. by building factories overseas
   ○ C. by buying materials from other countries
   ○ D. by introducing the moving assembly line

2. What was the decision of the U.S. Supreme Court in *Brown v. Board of Education of Topeka, Kansas*?
   ○ A. Separate but equal schools are constitutional.
   ○ B. Separate educational facilities are unequal.
   ○ C. Public education must be provided for all.
   ○ D. Public education must be supported by tax revenue.

3. César Chávez fought for the rights of which group of people?
   ○ A. farmworkers
   ○ B. former slaves
   ○ C. child laborers
   ○ D. garment workers

4. Which of these initiated the civil rights movement of the 1960s?
   ○ A. *The Feminine Mystique*
   ○ B. the Fourteenth Amendment
   ○ C. the Montgomery Bus Boycott
   ○ D. the United Farm Workers strike

5. What aspect of women's lives was **most** changed by the National Organization for Women?
   ○ A. employment opportunities
   ○ B. equitable wages
   ○ C. property rights
   ○ D. voting rights

6. What was an effect of the increase in car ownership in the United States?
   ○ A. People traveled less.
   ○ B. Gas stations were built.
   ○ C. The railroad system expanded.
   ○ D. Fewer people worked in factories.

7. All of these contributed to the shift from a manufacturing to a service economy in the United States **except**
   ○ A. automation.
   ○ B. the computer.
   ○ C. globalization.
   ○ D. the assembly line.

8. What is the **main** focus of people who are known as knowledge workers?
   ○ A. ideas and information
   ○ B. teaching and counseling
   ○ C. unions and equal rights
   ○ D. trade and manufacturing

9. Which of these are considered examples of mass media?

○ A. automobiles
○ B. televisions
○ C. airplanes
○ D. unions

10. Which of these was positively affected by the automobile industry in the early 1900s?

○ A. civil rights
○ B. mass media
○ C. globalization
○ D. employment

11. Which event marked the establishment of the United States as a world power?

○ A. Cold War
○ B. World War I
○ C. Industrial Revolution
○ D. collapse of the Soviet Union

12. The Cold War was a struggle for power between the United States and

○ A. Canada.
○ B. Germany.
○ C. the Middle East.
○ D. the Soviet Union.

13. Which term applies to a political system in which property and the economy are controlled by the government?

○ A. capitalism
○ B. monarchy
○ C. democracy
○ D. communism

14. How has U.S. political life changed over the last several decades?

○ A. Leadership has become more diverse.
○ B. Laws have restricted eligible voters.
○ C. Fewer people run for elected office.
○ D. Congress has fewer members.

15. Which innovation has helped to create an economy based on information?

○ A. radio
○ B. airplane
○ C. computer
○ D. automation

16. Which statement portrays the **most** effective response to the challenges of the 21st century?

○ A. The United States is responsible for solving the problems facing the world.
○ B. The problems facing the world will resolve themselves with the passing of time.
○ C. The global community must work together to solve world problems.
○ D. The problems of today are far worse than those of the past.

Applying Social Studies Skills

Use the excerpt below and your knowledge of history to answer the questions.

The Civil Rights Act of 1964

TITLE II: Injunctive Relief Against Discrimination in Places of Public Accommodation

Sec. 201.

(a) All persons shall be entitled to the full and equal enjoyment of the goods, services facilities, privileges, advantages, and accommodations of any place of public accommodation, as defined in this section, without discrimination or segregation on the ground of race, color, religion, or national origin.

(b) Each of the following establishments which serves the public is a place of public accommodation . . .

> (1) any inn, motel, or other establishment which provides lodging to transient guests . . .
> (2) any restaurant, cafeteria, lunch room, lunch counter, soda fountain, or other facility principally engaged in selling food for consumption on the premises . . .
> (3) any motion picture house, theater, concert hall, sports arena, stadium or other place of exhibition or entertainment . . .

---

17. What is the goal of Section 201 of the Civil Rights Act of 1964?
- ○ A. to provide voting rights for all
- ○ B. to end public school segregation
- ○ C. to create more diverse workplaces
- ○ D. to make public facilities available to all

18. What was happening in the United States that led to the passage of this law?

19. Based on Section 201, public accommodation includes
- ○ A. apartment buildings.
- ○ B. entertainment places.
- ○ C. educational facilities.
- ○ D. government buildings.

Exploring the Essential Question

What changes since 1914 have shaped how we live today?

Follow the directions to complete the item below.

20. Think about the events, innovations, and challenges addressed in this chapter. Write an essay describing how three of those events, innovations, or challenges have affected you personally and shaped how you live today. Make sure to convey your ideas clearly, using standard English.

Unit 9 Timeline Challenge Cards

U.S. Purchase of Alaska
1867

Many Americans originally thought of this acquisition as a "folly," but the nation soon discovered a wealth of resources in Alaska.

The Grange Promotes the Farmers' Cause
1870s

This self-help organization for farmers becomes a major force in politics and reform during the 1870s.

Congress Creates Yosemite National Park
1890

The preservation of Yosemite in California is one of the first major victories in a national conservation movement to protect the American wilderness for future generations.

U.S. Annexation of Hawaii
1898

After years of debate, the United States makes Hawaii a territory with the support of President McKinley. Queen Liliuokalani is the last Hawaiian monarch to rule the islands.

Spanish-American War
1898

The United States enters a four-month-long war with Spain. After a U.S. victory, Cuba declares independence from Spain, and Puerto Rico and the Philippines come under U.S. rule. A revolt against the United States in the Philippines lasts three more years. The Philippines become independent in 1947.

Andrew Carnegie Becomes Philanthropist
1901

Andrew Carnegie sells his steel company for $250 million and retires to a life of philanthropy. He and other industrialists, like John D. Rockefeller, use their fortunes to build universities, hospitals, libraries, and concert halls to benefit the American people.

United States Takes Over Canal Zone
1903

Panama cedes a 10-mile-wide "canal zone" to the United States. During the next two decades, the United States oversees the construction of the Panama Canal, which opens in 1921.

Child Labor Draws to a Close
1909

By year's end, 43 of the nation's 46 states outlaw child labor.

Founding of the NAACP
1909

W. E. B. Du Bois and other civil rights activists found the National Association for the Advancement of Colored People to ensure equal rights and opportunity for all African Americans.

U.S. Government Breaks Up Standard Oil
1911

President Roosevelt has John D. Rockefeller and his company investigated for unfair practices. The company's monopoly of the oil industry ends, and many other companies' monopolies over other industries are investigated.

United States Enters World War I
1917

U.S. forces side with and ultimately bring victory for the Allied powers. Three years later, the U.S. Senate tries to avoid involvement in future wars by rejecting the Treaty of Versailles, pushing the nation once again toward isolationism.

Nineteenth Amendment Ratified
1920

Ratification of the Nineteenth Amendment grants women the right to vote.

SOCIAL STUDIES SKILLS TOOLKIT

TCI's mission is to empower educators to help all learners succeed in the diverse classroom. Recognizing that some students may benefit from extra support, the following writing, reading, critical thinking skills, and map skills toolkits provide information and practice exercises to build student competence and confidence in these areas. Handouts with samples and graphic organizer templates will guide students in applying their skills for success in all their studies.

To the Teacher

Essay writing is an essential skill for success in school. This Writing Toolkit provides basic tools for supporting students who need help writing a five-paragraph expository or persuasive essay. It includes the following:

- graphic organizers for planning five-paragraph essays
- a sample persuasive essay
- instructional pages on the parts of a five-paragraph essay
- an overview of the writing process
- instructional pages on the writing process
- an essay scoring rubric

Using the Graphic Organizer to Improve Student Writing

Graphic organizers are useful for generating, organizing, and evaluating ideas at various stages of the writing process. The graphic organizers in this toolkit are easy-to-follow templates that can be applied to a variety of expository and persuasive writing assignments. The organizers follow the standard five-paragraph essay format—introduction, three body paragraphs, and conclusion—and contain prompts to remind students of the essential elements of each type of essay.

Tips for Teaching Students to Use the Graphic Organizer

- On a blank transparency, demonstrate how to construct the graphic organizer while students draw and label one in their notebooks. Discuss each part of an essay.
- Use color to help students differentiate between the parts of an essay. Project a transparency of the graphic organizer and circle or highlight each part of the essay using a different color. Suggest that when drafting their essays, students might want to write or highlight the various parts of the essay in different colors.
- Remind students that they can use a graphic organizer at any stage of the writing process. They should not worry about filling it in with polished prose or even complete sentences.
- Have students identify the type of essay in this toolkit. As needed, remind students that letters to the editor are persuasive. Review writing purposes, including the differences between writing that explains and writing that persuades.
- Project or hand out the sample essay to pairs of students. Have students use the essay to complete the Organizer for a Five-Paragraph Essay That Persuades.

Organizer for a Five-Paragraph Essay That Explains

Topic:

Paragraph 1 Introduction	Thesis statement:
Paragraph 2 Body	Topic sentence/Main idea 1: Support (Evidence/Explanation):
Paragraph 3 Body	Topic sentence/Main idea 2: Support (Evidence/Explanation):
Paragraph 4 Body	Topic sentence/Main idea 3: Support (Evidence/Explanation):
Paragraph 5 Conclusion	Summary:

Organizer for a Five-Paragraph Essay That Persuades

Topic:

Paragraph 1 Introduction	Thesis statement or Opinion:
Paragraph 2 Body	Topic sentence/Reason 1: Support (Evidence/Explanation):
Paragraph 3 Body	Topic sentence/Reason 2: Support (Evidence/Explanation):
Paragraph 4 Body	Topic sentence/Reason 3: Support (Evidence/Explanation):
Paragraph 5 Conclusion	Call to Action:

Sample Five-Paragraph Essay

JOIN THE MICROLENDING CLUB

What would your life be like if you had to live on less than two dollars a day? Two years ago, that's all that Ameena Iqbal earned. On that money, she had to feed, clothe, and shelter herself and three children in a small village in Bangladesh. Luckily, Iqbal had a talent and a dream. She could sew, and she dreamed of having a sewing machine. Her dream came true when a microlending club in Lewiston, North Carolina, lent her $200. That sum covered the cost of buying a sewing machine and renting space in a small shop with electricity. With that loan, Iqbal and her children were on their way out of poverty. Would you like to help people like Ameena Iqbal in leaving poverty behind? You can! Just join the Willow Glen Middle School Microlending Club.

You should join the Willow Glen Microlending Club because we help poor people around the world. Here's how it works. We raise money to lend. The money goes into a fund managed by an investment company. The money manager makes loans to poor people in other countries. Most of them are women who want to start or improve small businesses. The women get the money, along with a schedule for repaying it slowly over time. As the money is repaid, it goes back into the fund, little by little, with interest. Then our club uses the same money, plus other money we raise, to help more people. So far our club has helped six people, including a woman in India who started a bakery and a woman in Bolivia who improved her weaving business. In both these cases, the women's lives have changed completely. They have gone from barely being able to feed their children to paying their bills and making small improvements in their lives. Perhaps best of all, their children have a better chance in life as a result.

Some people aren't sure they want to join our club because they have to fund-raise. Don't let that stop you! The fundraising part of our work is easy. We sell a terrific product: rain barrels. The rain barrels collect rain, and people use them in their yards and gardens. Rain barrels are a great way to cut down on outdoor water use. We actually help our environment at the same time that we help people around the world. Best of all, the rain barrels just about sell themselves. People see what a good idea they are, as well as what a good cause they support. After some of our members sold two rain barrels on Alameda Street, they got three orders for barrels from neighbors on the same street just by word of mouth. People in our town want these barrels.

Another reason to join our club is that it's fun to be a member. We work in teams or small groups to sell the rain barrels. No one has to do the work alone, and you get to know people as you earn money for the club. Also, every time we make a loan, we have a small party to celebrate. That helps you make new friends in the club at the same time that you help poor people around the globe. The best part of all is seeing pictures of the people we help. You have no idea how good it can feel to see a picture of a small bakery in India that your efforts helped to start!

If you want to help others and have fun too, come to the next meeting of the Microlending Club. We meet in Room 216 on Wednesday right after school. Find out why our club already has 26 members and is growing bigger every month. Find out how easy it is to be a member. Most of all, find out how you can start helping to make the world a better place.

Camila Suarez, President
Jaquon Washington, Treasurer

Developing a Thesis Statement

Developing a Thesis Statement for Writing That Explains

When you write to explain, your **thesis statement** should summarize the central idea of your entire essay. A thesis statement is usually one sentence. It often appears at the end of your introduction.

You can develop a thesis statement before you begin drafting or afterward. For example, you may be asked to explain why a period of time is called a golden age. You come up with these reasons: (1) There was peace. (2) There was prosperity. (3) Many great accomplishments were made in the arts and sciences. You might then put your reasons together to write your thesis: This period was known as the golden age because it was a time of peace and prosperity, and many great accomplishments were made in the arts and sciences.

Here are some suggestions to help you develop a thesis statement for writing that explains:

- If the essay assignment asks a question, make your answer the thesis statement.
- Take some notes on the essay topic before developing your thesis statement.
- Be sure that your thesis statement presents an overview of what you will say in your body paragraphs.

Developing a Thesis Statement for Writing That Persuades

In a persuasive essay, your purpose is to convince the reader to agree with your thesis. To develop a thesis, consider your topic carefully: what do you think about it and why? You might need to do some research, since forming an opinion on an issue or topic requires that you know something about it. Your thesis statement should clearly state the position you plan to argue.

Here are some suggestions to help you develop a thesis statement for writing that persuades:

- Take some notes on the issue before developing your thesis statement.
- Avoid stating a fact as a thesis. Your thesis should be a judgment you make about an issue.
- Avoid making an all-or-nothing or exaggerated claim that is difficult to support. Use qualifying words such as *almost, often, rarely, usually,* or *most.*

Writing the Introduction

The **introduction,** or opening paragraph, prepares the audience for reading your essay. It "hooks" the reader's interest, gives background information on the issue or topic you plan to discuss, and presents your **thesis statement** or opinion statement.

The introduction is your chance to get the reader's attention. The way you do this depends on your purpose for writing. For a persuasive essay or editorial, consider these possibilities:

- a quotation
- a brief story
- a striking statistic
- a question
- an interesting or shocking fact

This first sentence creates interest by asking a question and using a striking statistic.

The **thesis** (or **opinion statement**) states your opinion.

What would your life be like if you had to live on less than two dollars a day? Two years ago, that's all that Ameena Iqbal earned. On that money, she had to feed, clothe, and shelter herself and three children in a small village in Bangladesh. Luckily, Iqbal had a talent and a dream. She could sew, and she dreamed of having a sewing machine. Her dream came true when a microlending club in Lewiston, North Carolina, lent her $200. That sum covered the cost of buying a sewing machine and renting space in a small shop with electricity. With that loan, Iqbal and her children were on their way out of poverty. Would you like to help people like Ameena Iqbal in leaving poverty behind? You can! Just join the Willow Glen Middle School Microlending Club.

Use this checklist when writing your introduction:
- Does my introduction create interest in the topic of my essay?
- Does my introduction summarize the arguments I plan to make?
- Does my introduction contain a clear statement of my thesis?

Writing Body Paragraphs

Use the body of your essay to support your thesis. In an essay that explains, each body paragraph presents a main idea that supports the thesis, as well as explanation and evidence. In a persuasive essay, each body paragraph gives a reason to support your proposition or opinion and explains and supports it.

The key elements of a body paragraph are the **topic sentence** and **support**. Support takes two main forms. The first form is **evidence,** such as facts, statistics, examples, or quotations that back up your thesis or help prove your proposition. The second form of support is **explanation,** statements that make your main ideas and evidence more understandable to your audience.

> The **topic sentence** states the main idea or argument.

> **Explanation** helps the audience understand how the club works.

> **Evidence** tells whom the club has already helped and how the club has helped them.

You should join the Willow Glen Microlending Club because we help poor people around the world. Here's how it works. We raise money to lend. The money goes into a fund managed by an investment company. The money manager makes loans to poor people in other countries. Most of them are women who want to start or improve small businesses. The women get the money, along with a schedule for repaying it slowly over time. As the money is repaid, it goes back into the fund, little by little, with interest! Then our club uses the same money, plus other money we raise, to help more people. So far our club has helped six people, including a woman in India who started a bakery and a woman in Bolivia who improved her weaving business. In both these cases, the women's lives have changed completely. They have gone from barely being able to feed their children to paying their bills and making small improvements in their lives. Perhaps best of all, their children have a better chance in life as a result.

Use this checklist when writing the body of your essay:
- Does each body paragraph include a topic sentence and support?
- Does each body paragraph focus on one main idea (if you are explaining) or one reason (if you are persuading)?
- Does each topic sentence relate clearly to the thesis statement?
- Do you fully explain all your ideas so that the audience can follow them?

Writing a Topic Sentence

The **topic sentence** states the main idea of a paragraph. A good topic sentence is clear and provides an overview of the sentences that will follow in the paragraph.

The topic sentence is usually, but not always, the first sentence of a paragraph. In a paragraph that explains, the topic sentence states a main idea. In a paragraph that persuades, the topic sentence states a reason.

Some people aren't sure they want to join our club because they have to fundraise. Don't let that stop you! The fundraising part of our work is easy. We sell a terrific product: rain barrels. The rain barrels collect rain, and people use them in their yards and gardens. Rain barrels are a great way to cut down on outdoor water use. We actually help our environment at the same time that we help people around the world. Best of all, the rain barrels just about sell themselves. People see what a good idea they are, as well as what a good cause they support. After some of our members sold two rain barrels on Alameda Street, they got three orders for barrels from neighbors on the same street just by word of mouth. People in our town want these barrels.

The **topic sentence** states a reason why students should join the club.

The supporting sentences tell how the club fundraises and why the fundraising is easy.

Use this checklist when writing your topic sentences:
- If I am writing to explain, does my topic sentence state the main idea of the paragraph?
- If I am writing to persuade, does my topic sentence state a reason that supports my thesis, or opinion?

Developing Body Paragraphs:
Supporting Evidence

Always support your ideas. In each body paragraph, you must present **evidence** to support each of your topic sentences and, therefore, your main point. Your evidence may include facts, statistics, examples, and quotations from various sources. In persuasive writing, you might also include stories, eyewitness accounts, or personal accounts. The following types of evidence appear in the letter to the editor about joining the microlending club:

Fact: The money goes into a fund managed by an investment company.

Statistic: So far our club has helped six people.

Examples: . . . a woman in India who started a bakery business and a woman in Bolivia who improved her weaving business.

Personal account: After some of our members sold two rain barrels on Alameda Street, they got three orders for barrels from neighbors on the same street just by word of mouth.

Use this checklist when presenting your supporting evidence:
- Do I provide evidence to support each topic sentence?
- Is my supporting evidence clear? If I am writing to persuade, is my supporting evidence convincing?

Developing Body Paragraphs: Explanation

Always explain your ideas. You are writing for an audience that probably does not know everything you know about your topic. Even if your readers do know something about the topic, they may not understand every statement you make about it. Furthermore, no matter how good your support is, it will usually be better if you explain it.

In the paragraph below, suppose the writer simply said, "It's fun to be a member." Why should the audience believe it? Why wouldn't the audience ask, "What kind of fun do you have?" By giving explanations, the writer anticipates what the audience will want to know.

> Another reason to join our club is that it's fun to be a member. We work in teams or small groups to sell the rain barrels. No one has to do the work alone, and you get to know people as you earn money for the club. Also, every time we make a loan, we have a small party to celebrate. That helps you make new friends in the club at the same time that you help poor people around the globe. The best part of all is seeing pictures of the people we help. You have no idea how good it can feel to see a picture of a small bakery in India that your efforts helped to start!

In a persuasive essay, you can also explain by considering the reader's objections and addressing them. In the paragraph below, notice how the writer considers and then addresses an objection a reader might raise: that fundraising is hard.

> Some people aren't sure they want to join our club because they have to fundraise. Don't let that stop you! The fundraising part of our work is easy. We sell a terrific product, rain barrels. The rain barrels collect rain, and people use them in their yards and gardens. Rain barrels are a great way to cut down on outdoor water use. We actually help our environment at the same time that we help people around the world. Best of all, the rain barrels just about sell themselves. People see what a good idea they are, as well as what a good cause they support. After some of our members sold two rain barrels on Alameda Street, they got three orders for barrels from neighbors on the same street just by word of mouth. People in our town want these barrels.

In a persuasive essay, explanation can help persuade the reader.

Use this checklist when writing your explanation:
- Do I anticipate questions the reader might have and answer them?
- If I am writing to persuade, do I consider the reader's objections or opposing views and then address them?

Writing the Conclusion

The last paragraph of your essay is the **conclusion**. Your goal in this paragraph is to leave your reader feeling that you have pulled everything together in a convincing way. If you are writing to explain, end with a summary of your main ideas, but do not use the exact same words you have already used. If you are writing to persuade, end with a **call to action**.

> If you want to help others and have fun too, come to the next meeting of the Microlending Club. We meet in Room 216 on Wednesday right after school. Find out why our club already has 26 members and is growing bigger every month. Find out how easy it is to be a member. Most of all, find out how you can start helping to make the world a better place.

End with a **call to action**; that is, tell your reader what to do or think.

Add important details, provide emphasis, or appeal to people's consciences.

To be effective, a conclusion must do more than simply summarize and restate. It should also contain something new—a fresh idea or connection, an additional piece of information, some striking language—to keep readers engaged to the very end.

Here are some other ideas for crafting an effective conclusion:
- End with a question that will keep readers thinking.
- Acknowledge a final opposing viewpoint and argue against it convincingly.
- End with a fitting quotation.
- Appeal to your reader's sense of what is right and good.

Use this checklist when writing your conclusion:
- Did I remind the reader of my central idea and purpose for writing without using the exact same words?
- Did I pull everything together in a convincing way?

Overview of the Writing Process

Good writing is the result of a multistep process that takes time and practice. The writing process can be divided into stages: **prewriting, drafting, revising,** and **finalizing**. Each stage consists of several steps. You can adjust the writing process to suit your writing assignment. Feel free to backtrack to an earlier stage or rearrange the order of steps as you write. Here is one way to look at the writing process.

Stage 1: Prewriting
- Come up with a topic or gather ideas about a topic you were assigned.
- Develop a thesis about that topic.
- Research and gather information to support your thesis.
- Evaluate your sources.
- Plan your essay using a graphic organizer.

Stage 2: Drafting
- Use the graphic organizer as a guide but add or change ideas as you go along.
- Write an engaging introduction that includes your thesis.
- Use each body paragraph to develop one main idea or one reason related to your thesis.
- Use your conclusion to sum up in fresh words or to issue a call to action.

Stage 3: Revising
- Reread your draft and identify places that need improvement.
- Rewrite, reorganize, and add or delete material if necessary.
- Edit your writing for accurate content, clear sentences, helpful transitions, and effective word choices.
- Consult with peer reviewers.
- Evaluate suggested changes and make revisions.

Stage 4: Finalizing
- Proofread for errors in spelling, grammar, usage, and mechanics.
- Make corrections.
- If needed, make a bibliography or source list.
- Use correct formatting. Your paper should have margins on all sides. Paragraphs should be indented. Everything should appear orderly and consistent on the page.
- Create a final copy.

Prewriting: Using Primary and Secondary Sources

Historians and researchers divide historical sources into two types: primary and secondary.

Primary sources are documents or recordings that were created at the same time that the events being described were taking place. An example of a primary source about the Civil War is a letter written by a soldier to his family during the Civil War. Artifacts and printed material from a historical era, such as sheet music and advertisements, are also considered primary sources.

Secondary sources are documents or recordings that were created after the events being described were over. Secondary sources interpret and synthesize primary sources and other types of information. An example of a secondary source about the Civil War is a television documentary created by a 20th-century filmmaker.

Other kinds of primary and secondary sources are listed below.

Primary Sources
Diaries, journals, and logs
Letters
Speeches
Interviews and oral histories
Memoirs
Autobiographies
Magazine and newspaper articles
Photographs
Home movies
Field notes
Sheet music
Paintings
Artifacts

Secondary Sources
Biographies
Government and organizational records
Statistical records
Editorials
Magazine and newspaper articles
Encyclopedias, almanacs, and other
    reference works
Nonfiction books
Television and film documentaries
Public opinion polls

Prewriting: Taking Notes and Citing Sources

If you research your topic, take notes. Be sure to record the sources of your information. If you are using Internet resources, print out relevant material from the Web sites. If you are using print resources, take notes. Always keep track of the title, author, publisher, date of publication, page numbers, and Web address of any source you use.

Use a copy of this page for each source. Use the bottom (and the back if necessary) to take notes.

Title: _____

Author(s): _____

Publisher and copyright date: _____

Pages used: _____

Internet address: _____

Is it a primary or a secondary source? _____

What information does this source provide about my topic?

Prewriting: Evaluating Evidence

To be persuasive in your essay, you will need to provide relevant and accurate evidence to back up your position. You can use facts, statistics, examples, reasons, quotations, and anecdotes. To recognize useful evidence, ask these questions:

Is the information **relevant**?
- How closely is the information related to the topic of my essay?
- Does the information help me support my opinion?

Is the information **complete**?
- Does the author appear to tell only part of the story or only some of the facts?

Is the information **accurate**?
- Who wrote it? Is that person an expert? When was it written?
- Can I find this same information in books and on Web sites that are made by the government, by museums, and by people who are experts in their field?

Prewriting: Evaluating Sources

As you conduct research on your essay topic, you may come across sources that are not completely accurate. Keep the following information in mind:

Is the author or publication biased? A biased source lacks objectivity and displays a slanted point of view. An author's viewpoint can be influenced by many factors, such as politics, gender, and ethnic background. Publications can be similarly influenced. Here are questions to help you determine the extent to which bias may affect the accuracy of your source:

- Why was this source created? Is it meant to inform, entertain, or persuade?
- Do the author and publisher have a reputation for accuracy?
- Does the author or publisher provide a bibliography of sources?
- Does the source include all relevant facts?
- Does the source include statements of opinion?
- Does the source use questionable claims as supporting evidence?
- Does the source use loaded language to try to provoke an emotional response?
- Does the source make broad generalizations that cannot be supported by evidence?
- Does the source acknowledge other points of view?

Is the source out of date? Older sources, particularly primary sources, are often extremely valuable because they take you back in time and provide details that only someone there at the time could have known. Still, they may contain inaccuracies. Recent sources are usually better for essays on current topics or fast-moving issues. Find out when your source material was written or published. Be sure the date is appropriate for your purpose.

Prewriting: Planning Your Essay

Before you draft your essay, you need to plan how you will arrange your main ideas or your reasons. In an essay that explains, you will usually want to select the most logical order. For example, you might sequence according to chronological order or state a cause and then each of its effects. In an essay that persuades, writers often present their best, or most important, reason first or save their best, or most important, reason for last.

Here are other questions to consider as you arrange the order of your paragraphs, as well as your support:

- How are my main ideas related? Present them in a logical order that makes the relationship clear.
- Does the reader have to understand one idea in order to understand another? If so, present the most fundamental idea first.
- Are my main ideas or reasons obvious, or are they difficult to understand? Consider placing the idea or reason that is easiest for the reader to grasp first. Then draw the reader into more difficult ideas.

Once you have decided on a plan, use the appropriate graphic organizer to map out exactly what you are going to say in each paragraph. You do not have to fill it in with complete sentences if you don't want to. But do include enough information to make the order of your reasons or main ideas, as well as your support, clear.

Drafting: Writing Clearly

Good writing is always clear and easy to follow. The first step in clear writing is always thinking about your audience. Ask yourself what your audience already knows. You do not have to repeat familiar ideas. Also ask yourself what your audience doesn't know or might want to know about your topic. In addition, focus on the following points:

To write clearly and to make your writing easy to read,
- develop one idea at a time. Follow your graphic organizer.
- make sure each sentence in a paragraph relates to the main idea or reason.
- make sure each paragraph relates to the thesis.
- leave out unnecessary details.
- use transitions to show how your ideas relate to one another.
- don't be afraid to repeat key words and phrases.
- be aware of your tone. Tone reflects your attitude toward your subject.
- use the passive voice only when the doer of the action is not known or is not important. The active voice is generally stronger, more concise, and easier to understand.
- use specific, concrete language.
- use a variety of sentence lengths and types.

Revising: Improving Your Essay

Once you have finished your draft, it is time to step back and evaluate your work. Follow these steps for revision:

- Take a break after writing the draft. Come back to it with fresh eyes.
- Remember the purpose of your essay by rereading your assignment.
- Reread your essay. Read it silently and then read it aloud.
- Mark the places that seem to need improvement.
- Rewrite and edit, making all necessary changes. Use the checklist and writing tips below.
- Proofread for errors in spelling, grammar, usage, and punctuation.

Essay Checklist

- Does my essay include a well-written introduction and conclusion?
- Do I state my thesis clearly in the introduction?
- Does each body paragraph have a topic sentence that supports my thesis?
- Does each body paragraph explain and support the topic sentence?

Writing Tips

- If your essay seems disorganized, go back to your graphic organizer. Did you follow your plan? If so, think about how to reorganize your material to make your essay more orderly and logical. Move, add, or delete material as necessary.
- Look for places to add or improve transitions. Transitional words and phrases include *before, after, finally, most of all, first, last, like, unlike, likewise, nevertheless, in contrast, because, therefore, since, for that reason, and, also, furthermore, for example,* and *in other words.* Use transitions to link paragraphs and to link sentences.
- Look for places to vary your sentence length and structure. Use both short and long sentences. Insert an occasional question if it works. Begin your sentences in different ways.
- Vary your word choice. Replace dull words such as *good, great, bad, awful, terrific, awesome, excellent, really,* and *very* with more precise words. Replace state of being verbs (such as *is, are, was,* and *were*) with action verbs.

Revising: Giving and Getting Feedback from Peers

A helpful way to get feedback on your writing is by sharing your work with a classmate. Peer review works best when both individuals know their roles.

Writer's Role	Reviewer's Role
• Bring a copy of your revised draft. • Don't explain your purpose or your plan before the reader has read your paper. • Share any concerns you have about your writing. • Respond thoughtfully. Try not to be defensive since that might keep your reader from providing complete or honest feedback. • If you want more feedback, be sure to ask for it.	• Read carefully. Write your comments on the draft for the writer to keep. • Ask thoughtful questions. • Try to address the particular concerns the writer has expressed. • Be as positive and truly helpful as you can be. Give praise as well as suggestions for improvement. • Be honest.

Tips for Reviewing

- Ask questions that require more than a "yes" or "no" answer. This will help the writer to say more about his or her writing.
- If you like something about the essay, say so. Positive feedback shows the writer what he or she has done well. This is as helpful as criticism in learning to improve one's writing.
- Be specific. For example, "When I got to this sentence, I got confused" is more helpful than "This part is confusing."
- Criticize the writing, not the writer. Begin your comments with "I," not "You" or "Your essay." This helps keep the writer from feeling hurt or defensive.
- Write your comments on the draft, but don't edit or make changes. It is the writer's decision whether to incorporate your suggestions or not.

Essay Rubric

Use this rubric to help you evaluate your own and others' essays.

Criteria	Score			
	4	**3**	**2**	**1**
Purpose	Essay achieves its purpose (to persuade or explain).	Essay achieves its purpose reasonably well.	Essay struggles to achieve its purpose.	Essay does not achieve its purpose.
Organization	Ideas are clear and logically organized.	Ideas are reasonably clear and logically organized.	Ideas are somewhat unclear and disorganized.	Ideas are unclear and disorganized.
Content	Essay provides rich and detailed support for its main ideas or reasons.	Essay provides detailed support for its main ideas or reasons.	Essay provides support for its main ideas or reasons.	Essay does not provide support for its main ideas or reasons.
Style and Conventions	Writing varies word choice and sentence structure appropriately. It has no grammar, spelling, or mechanical errors.	Writing generally varies word choice and sentence structure appropriately. It has few grammar, spelling, or mechanical errors.	Writing does not vary word choice or sentence structure. It has some grammar, spelling, or mechanical errors.	Writing misuses words or has faulty sentences. It has many grammar, spelling, or mechanical errors.

SCORE:

To the Teacher

Reading skills are critical to students' success in all areas of study. In social studies, students will have great difficulty learning and understanding history if they struggle with reading comprehension.

This Reading Toolkit provides basic tools for supporting students who need additional guidance and structure. It includes
- a Prereading Guide that can be used before any chapter.
- instructional pages on understanding organizational text patterns.
- instructional pages that develop comprehension strategies.
- instructional pages that focus on vocabulary development.

Make the following pages available to your students as an independent tutorial, for class instruction, or for use with peer tutoring.

Prereading Guide

What is the **title** of the chapter?

List the section heads and the key terms below.

Section Heads   **Key Terms**

Quickly sketch or describe three **images** from the chapter. Write a one-sentence caption that explains how you think each image relates to the chapter.

Based on the information above, what predictions can you make about the main idea of the chapter?

Read the **chapter summary**. Write one sentence that explains what you think is the main idea of the chapter.

Ask questions to help focus and guide your reading.

Organizational Text Patterns

Expository texts, such as chapters in textbooks, have different organizational patterns. These patterns, or structures, can often be identified by **signal words**.

Text Pattern: Cause and Effect

What is it? Text organized to show cause and effect identifies the reasons that events occur and their results.

How to do it. Signal words that help identify a cause and effect pattern include the following:

as a result	because	consequently	due to
effects of	for	for this reason	hence
how	if . . . then	in order to	is caused by
leads to	may be due to	so	so that
thereby	therefore	thus	when . . . then

Try it. Read the following passage. Then list causes and effects in a graphic organizer like the one below.

> *As a result of the Civil War, many Americans began thinking of the United States as one country, rather than as a collection of sovereign states. Slavery no longer existed because of the war. There were terrible costs, though. Due to the war, more than 620,000 soldiers lay dead. Croplands lay in ruins. It would take generations for the South to recover.*

Graphic Organizer: Cause and Effect

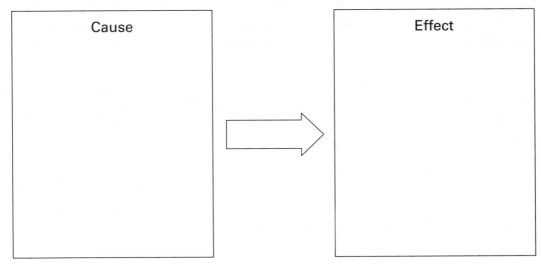

Cause

Effect

Organizational Text Patterns

Expository texts, such as chapters in textbooks, have different organizational patterns. These patterns, or structures, can often be identified by **signal words**.

Text Pattern: Compare and Contrast

What is it? Text with a compare and contrast organizational pattern tells about the similarities and differences of two or more objects, places, events, or ideas.

How to do it. Signal words that help identify a compare and contrast pattern include the following:

although	as well as	as opposed to	both
but	by contrast	compared with	different from
either . . . or	even though	however	instead of
in comparison	in the same way	just as	like
more . . . than	on the other hand	otherwise	similar to
similarly	still	unlike	yet

Try it. Read the following passage. Then list similarities and differences in a graphic organizer like the one below.

> *Both the Union and the Confederacy had advantages and disadvantages going into the Civil War. The North had a larger population and more factories and railroads than the South, but it lacked strong military leadership. The South had serious economic problems, but it had capable generals and the advantage of fighting a defensive war.*

Graphic Organizer: Compare and Contrast

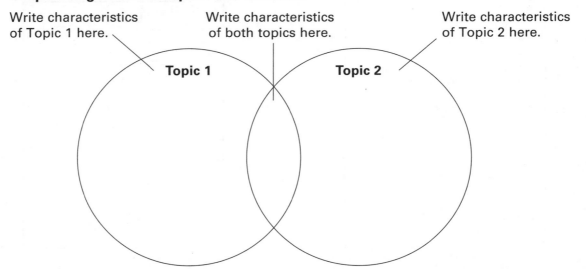

Write characteristics of Topic 1 here.

Write characteristics of both topics here.

Write characteristics of Topic 2 here.

Topic 1   Topic 2

Organizational Text Patterns

Expository texts, such as chapters in textbooks, have different organizational patterns. These patterns, or structures, can often be identified by **signal words**.

Text Pattern: Proposition and Support
What is it? Text with a proposition and support organizational pattern presents an argument with supporting examples.

How to do it. Signal words that help identify a proposition and support pattern include the following:

additionally	because	believe	clearly
conclusively	consider	first	for example
for instance	furthermore	generally	however
if . . . then	in fact	it could be argued	most convincing
never	not only . . . but	often	this means

Try it. Read the following passage. Then list a proposition and supporting examples in a graphic organizer like the one below.

The Articles of Confederation did not establish an effective form of government because Congress's powers were limited. Not only was Congress not allowed to impose taxes, but Congress had to ask the states for funds to do anything. Too often, the states ignored the requests. Additionally, Congress could not intervene to resolve disputes between individual states. It could be argued that Shays's Rebellion best shows the weaknesses of the Articles of Confederation. When a group of farmers seized the weapons at a national arsenal, Congress did not have an army to stop them. The state militia had to restore order.

Graphic Organizer: Proposition and Support

Proposition:
Support:
Support:
Support:

Organizational Text Patterns

Expository texts, such as chapters in textbooks, have different organizational patterns. These patterns, or structures, can often be identified by **signal words**.

Text Pattern: Sequencing

What is it? Text organized to show sequencing relates a series of events or steps in a process in time order.

How to do it. Signal words that help identify the sequencing pattern include the following:

after	afterward	before	during	earlier
finally	first	following	initially	last
later	meanwhile	next	not long after	now
previously	second	since	soon	then
third	today	until	when	

Try it. Read the following passage. Then show the sequence of events in a graphic organizer like the one below.

Article V of the U.S. Constitution lays out several methods for amending the Constitution. All but one of the Constitution's 27 amendments have followed the same process. First, a bill to amend the Constitution is proposed in Congress. Next, the amendment needs approval of a two-thirds majority of the House of Representatives. If it does not receive a two-thirds majority, the amendment process does not continue. After the House of Representatives has approved the amendment, the Senate must approve the amendment by a two-thirds majority. In some cases, amendments have passed the House of Representatives, but have not received enough votes in the Senate. If successful in both the House and the Senate, the amendment is then sent to the states for approval. At this point, three-quarters of the state legislatures must ratify the amendment in order for it to become law.

Graphic Organizer: Sequencing

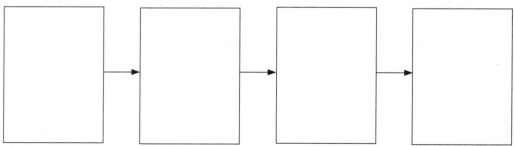

Comprehension Strategy

Comprehension strategies help you better understand and remember what you read.

KWL: Know / Want / Learned

Follow these steps to fill in the graphic organizer:

Step 1: Brainstorm what you know about the topic of the chapter.

Step 2: Create questions that show what you want to find out when you read this chapter.

Step 3: Read the chapter. Make a list of the important details that you learned.

What I Know	What I Want to Find Out	What I Learned

Comprehension Strategy

Comprehension strategies help you better understand and remember what you read.

REAP: Read / Encode / Annotate / Ponder

Follow these steps to complete the graphic organizer below as you read the chapter:

Step 1: Read (R) the text. Write the title of the chapter.

Step 2: Encode (E) the text. Use your own words to describe the main idea of the chapter.

Step 3: Annotate (A) the text. Summarize at least three important points from the chapter.

Step 4: Ponder (P) the text. Write down at least one question that you now have after reading this chapter.

R	E
A	**P**

Comprehension Strategy

Comprehension strategies help you better understand and remember what you read.

SQ3R: Survey / Question / Read / Recite / Review
Follow these steps to read the chapter:

Step 1: Survey the chapter by looking at the title, subheads, captions, and illustrations. Read the introduction.

Step 2: Question. Turn the title and subheads into questions to focus your reading. Look up the meaning of any new vocabulary.

Step 3: Read. Search for answers to your questions.

Step 4: Recite. Recite the answers to your questions aloud or in writing. Reread if you have any unanswered questions.

Step 5: Review. Look over the chapter and summarize what you have learned.

Vocabulary Development

Illustrated Dictionary

Chapter _____

Follow these steps to create an illustrated dictionary for your Key Content Terms:

Step 1: Choose a Key Content Term.

Step 2: Draw a diagram, word map, or other graphic organizer that shows how the term relates to something you already know or to another key term in this chapter or in a previous chapter. Write the term in bigger or darker letters than you use for any other words.

Step 3: Find the definition of each term, and summarize its meaning in your own words.

Step 4: Write a sentence that uses the term.

Step 5: Repeat for all the other Key Content Terms.

Sketch/Diagram	In Your Own Words	In a Sentence

Vocabulary Development

Rate Your Knowledge   **Chapter** _____

Follow these steps to rate your knowledge of the Key Content Terms:

Step 1: Use one spectrum for each Key Content Term. Rate your knowledge
of each term by marking the appropriate place on the spectrum.
Below the spectrum, write anything you know about the term.

Step 2: Find out what others know about each term by asking another person
(for example, a classmate, friend, parent, or teacher). Write down what
you learn on the back of this sheet or on a separate sheet of paper.

Step 3: Find the definition of each term. Then, on the back of this sheet or on
a separate sheet of paper, write a sentence that uses each term.

Term:				
1	**2**	**3**	**4**	**5**
Unfamiliar				Very familiar

Term:				
1	**2**	**3**	**4**	**5**
Unfamiliar				Very familiar

Term:				
1	**2**	**3**	**4**	**5**
Unfamiliar				Very familiar

Term:				
1	**2**	**3**	**4**	**5**
Unfamiliar				Very familiar

Vocabulary Development

Follow these guidelines to create a Word Grid for each of your Key Content Terms:

Box 1: List a Key Content Term from the chapter.

Box 2: Find the definition of the term and summarize its meaning in your own words.

Box 3: Add *related* information, such as examples, facts, synonyms, sayings, or a category to which the word belongs.

Box 4: Add *contrasting* information, such as antonyms, or words with opposite meanings.

1. Key Content Term	**2.** In Your Own Words
3. Related Words or Ideas	**4.** Contrasting Words or Ideas

1. Key Content Term	**2.** In Your Own Words
3. Related Words or Ideas	**4.** Contrasting Words or Ideas

Vocabulary Development

Word Pyramid

Follow these guidelines to create a Word Pyramid for each Key Content Term:

Row 1: List a Key Content Term from the chapter.

Row 2: Describe the term in your own words.

Row 3: Compare the term to one thing it is similar to and contrast the term with one thing it is different from.

Row 4: Draw or list things that the word brings to mind. That is, "associate" the word with things you already know.

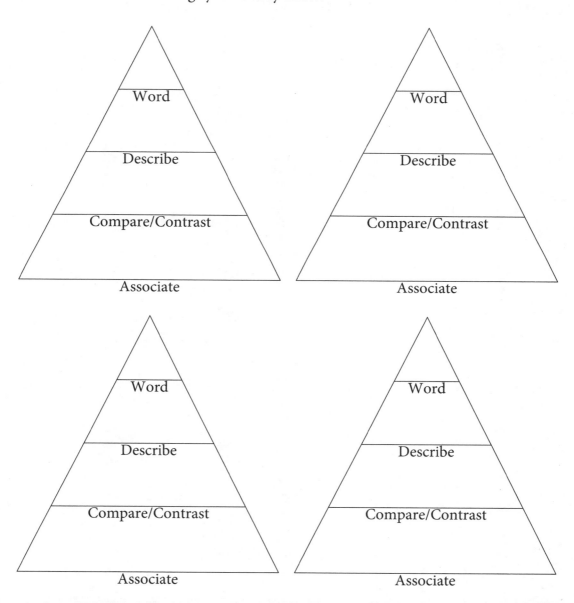

To the Teacher

Success in social studies depends on proficiency with fundamental critical thinking and reading skills. However, students may come into your class with varying levels of ability in comprehending social studies texts. Without fluency in such skills as recognizing cause and effect, students will have great difficulty in understanding history. You can use the pages in this toolkit to bring your students up to speed.

First check the skills correlation chart in the back of the Lesson Guide to see which skill or skills are part of the lesson you plan to teach. If you believe that your class would benefit from direct instruction in that skill, plan to dedicate some class time to the corresponding skill page of this toolkit. This extra bit of time will pay dividends in the success of the TCI activity and also in the long term, as these skills appear in state standards and are tested in state and national assessments.

Many teachers may want to make a transparency of the page and work through the exercise together with the class. Whole-class instruction such as this will give you the chance to model the skill for your students as well as provide them with the opportunity to practice it. You can also photocopy the page and distribute it to students for classwork or homework.

As you review students' work with them, be sure to ask them to explain how they reached their answers. This sort of "thinking out loud" will help students to become more conscious of their own thought processes. Listening to their classmates' explanations will also show students other ways to read for meaning.

Comparing and Contrasting

What is it? When you **compare** things, you look for ways they are alike. When you **contrast** things, you look for ways they are different.

How to do it. As you read, first identify the things you want to compare. Next, list all the ways they are alike. These similarities may be stated or they may be implied. Then list all the ways in which the things differ. These too may be state or implied. Organizing similarities and differences in a Venn diagram will let you compare and contrast at a glance.

Try it. Read the passage below. Identify the similarities and differences. Write the similarities in the overlapping area of a Venn diagram like the one below. Write the differences in the spaces on either side.

Athens and Sparta were both city-states of ancient Greece. Yet they differed greatly. Located near the sea, Athens grew large and powerful through trade. Athenians were eager to travel and exchange ideas with others. They made their city a center of art and culture.

Sparta, on the other hand, was an inland city. Spartans did not trust out-siders or their ideas. Instead of trade, they used their armies to take what they needed from their neighbors. Spartans valued strength and simplicity. They pro-duced
soldiers rather than artists and thinkers.

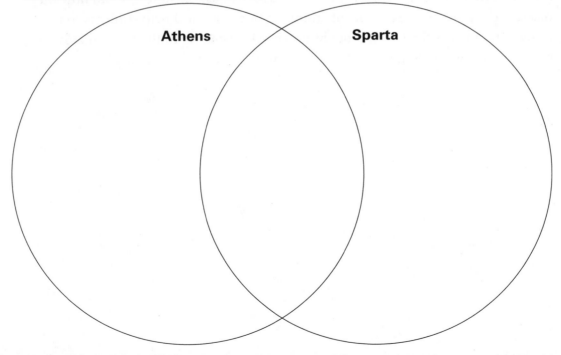

© Teachers' Curriculum Institute

Sequencing Events

What is it? **Sequencing** events means listing them in the order they occurred. Organizing events in time order will help you understand why things happened as they did.

How to do it. As you read, look for words that signal time relationships between events. These words include *first, next, then, during, later, finally, before, after, at the same time,* and *meanwhile.* Then say the order of events to yourself. Recording events in a flow chart will help you clarify the sequence.

Try it. Read the passage below and spot the words that signal time relationships. Then sequence the events in a flow chart like the one below.

> It took many years to become a knight in Europe in the Middle Ages. At age seven, a boy left home to live in the castle of a lord. He then became a page. During this time, he learned to ride a horse. After about seven years, he became a squire and took care of his lord's horse and weapons. At the same time, he trained to become a warrior and served his lord in battle.
>
> In his early 20s, a worthy squire would become a knight. Before receiving this honor, a squire often spent a night in prayer, and then dressed in white to show purity. In a ceremony, the young man promised loyalty to his lord. The lord then tapped him on each shoulder with a sword to make him a knight.

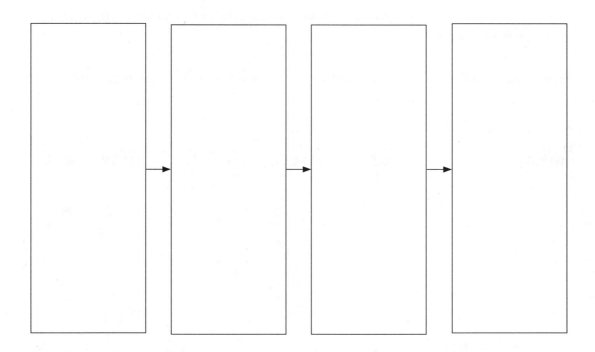

Creating a Timeline

What is it? A **timeline** shows when, and in what order, past events happened. Organizing events along a timeline helps you see how the events are related to one another in time. Understanding these relationships can also help you remember the sequence of events.

How to do it. First, locate the dates in your reading. Find the earliest and latest dates you want to record. Then choose beginning and end dates for your timeline. For example, if your dates range from 1812 to 1926, your timeline might begin at 1800 and end at 1930. Using a ruler, divide the line into equal units of time. Finally, place the other dated events from the reading along your timeline.

Try it. Read this passage and list dates to show on a timeline like the one below.

"All roads lead to Rome." This ancient saying dates back more than 2,000 years.

For 500 years, from about 27 B.C.E. to 476 C.E., Rome was the capital of the greatest empire the world had ever seen. At its height, around 117 C.E., the Roman Empire spanned the entire Mediterranean world.

However, the empire did not last. Power struggles, border threats, and economic and social problems led to its fall. In 330 C.E., the emperor Constantine moved his capital east to Byzantium. After that, power was divided between two emperors, one in Rome and the other in Byzantium. A Germanic tribe invaded Rome in 410 C.E. and looted the city. In 476 C.E., the last emperor in Rome was driven from his throne.

From your list of dates, create a timeline for the history of the Roman Empire.

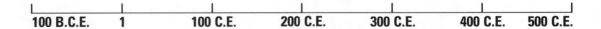

100 B.C.E.	1	100 C.E.	200 C.E.	300 C.E.	400 C.E.	500 C.E.

Analyzing Cause and Effect

What is it? A **cause** is something that brings about a particular result, which is called an **effect**. An event may have more than one cause and more than one effect. Analyzing cause and effect can help you understand why historical events happened.

Both causes and effects can be either **immediate** or **long-term**. An immediate cause or effect happens shortly before or after an event. Long-term causes and effects generally unfold over many months or years.

How to do it. To identify cause and effect, consider the following questions:
- What was the trigger that made an event happen? (immediate cause)
- What were the conditions that contributed to the event? (long-term cause)
- What was the direct result of an action? (immediate effect)
- What were some lasting consequences? (long-term effect)

Try it. Read this passage about the Boston Tea Party.

> *After the French and Indian War, British actions increasingly angered the American colonists. To pay for military costs, the British Parliament passed laws that chipped away at colonial rights. One such law, the Tea Act, set off a chain reaction that soon carried the colonies to open rebellion. To protest the Tea Act, a group of colonists dumped a shipload of tea into Boston Harbor. The outraged British clamped down with even harsher laws. Colonists called these laws the Intolerable Acts. These acts helped to build colonial resistance to the British government. This resistance led to the American Revolution.*

Fill in a chart like this one to show the causes and effects of the Boston Tea Party.

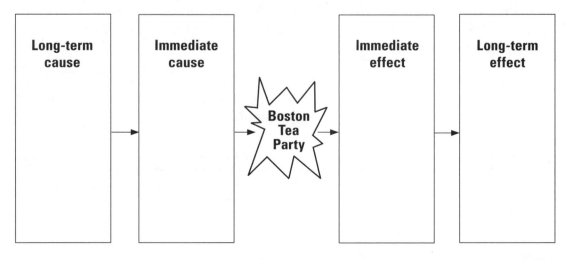

Critical Thinking Skills Toolkit **345**

Making Predictions

What is it? By analyzing cause and effect, you can often make **predictions**. Making predictions means making educated guesses about the likely outcome of certain events or actions.

How to do it. Here are three ways to make predictions:

1. Look for patterns. Do the causes and effects over time follow a regular pattern?

2. Consider what might come next in a sequence. Where does this chain of events seem to be leading?

3. Look for correlations (connections) between historical events. Are there other events in history or other places in the world with a similar situation?

Try it. Often new inventions trigger a chain of events with a variety of outcomes. Consider the example of the cotton gin.

> *In 1793, the United States produced about 180,000 pounds of cotton. Seventeen years later, the harvest had grown to an astounding 93 million pounds. What spurred this incredible change? It was Eli Whitney's invention of the cotton gin in 1793.*
>
> *The cotton gin is a machine that removes the seeds from cotton. Before the gin, one person took all day to clean one pound of cotton. In contrast, one small cotton gin could clean 50 pounds in a day. Later, horse-driven gins could clean thousands of pounds per week. With cotton in high demand by textile mills in the North and in Britain, it quickly became very profitable for southern farmers.*

Answer the questions to predict other impacts of the cotton gin.

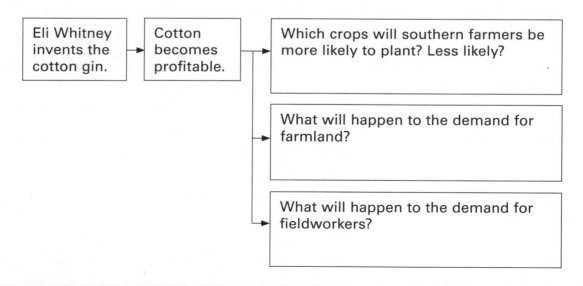

Eli Whitney invents the cotton gin. → Cotton becomes profitable. →

Which crops will southern farmers be more likely to plant? Less likely?

What will happen to the demand for farmland?

What will happen to the demand for fieldworkers?

Recognizing the Role of Chance, Error, and Oversight in History

What is it? Many things affect the course of history, even accidents and mistakes. **Chance** is an unexpected or accidental event. **Errors** are mistakes people make. **Oversight** occurs when someone does not pay close attention to what is important.

How to do it. Look for examples of chance, error, and oversight in your reading. What was the effect or outcome of each accident or error?

Try it. Read the following passage about the American Revolution. Notice any chance happenings, errors, or oversights.

> In 1777, the British planned to capture Albany, New York. Three British armies were to attack from different directions to take the city. By controlling Albany, they could prevent colonial forces from joining together.
>
> General Burgoyne to the north and Lieutenant Colonel St. Leger to the west set off as planned. However, General Howe to the south decided to attack Philadelphia before heading to Albany. Once his troops occupied Philadelphia, he stayed there. While Howe enjoyed the company of British supporters, George Washington attacked and prevented Howe's army from ever setting out for Albany.
>
> Meanwhile, Burgoyne was clumsily moving his army through the woods. He had planned for his army to live off the land, but his troops were an easy target for local militias. As a result, his men suffered from a lack of food and supplies. As for St. Leger, he was only partway to Albany when he was forced to retreat.
>
> With only limited troop strength in New York, the British lost the Battle of Saratoga later that year. It was the turning point of the war.

Identify two errors or oversights and their consequences. Can you think of a chance occurrence that might have changed the outcome?

Error or Oversight	Consequence
1. General Howe decided to attack Philadelphia instead of marching on.	1. Howe's army never got to Albany to support Burgoyne and St. Leger.
2.	2.
3.	3

Framing Questions to Research

What is it? **Framing questions** to research means identifying specific information you would like to know about a topic. When you frame a question, you focus your search for answers.

How to do it. As you read, think about what information is not stated. What questions do you have? Write them down. Then choose one question to start your research. Write down any new questions that come to mind as you learn more. You may need to revise your original question. If your question seems too broad, reframe it to focus your research.

Too broad: *What was the role of city planning in 20th-century America?*

More focused: *How did city planning help San Francisco recover after the earthquake of 1906?*

Try it. Read this passage.

> *Labor leader Mary Harris Jones, commonly known as Mother Jones, went to Pennsylvania in 1903. She was going to support a strike by 75,000 textile workers. To her surprise, she found that about 10,000 of the workers were children. Jones led a "March of the Mill Children" from Pennsylvania to Oyster Bay, New York. She petitioned President Theodore Roosevelt to support child labor laws.*
>
> *Mother Jones's march helped people across the country become aware of child labor. Reformers demanded an end to child labor. By 1909, 43 states had passed laws that outlawed the hiring of children.*

One question on the topic of child labor is suggested below. Frame three more questions for research on this topic. Which would be a good question to start researching?

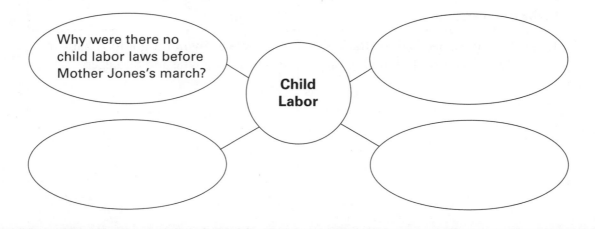

Why were there no child labor laws before Mother Jones's march?

Child Labor

© Teachers' Curriculum Institute

Distinguishing Fact from Opinion

What is it? Statements that can be proven to be true are **facts**. Statements that reflect someone's personal viewpoint are **opinions**. Recognizing the difference between fact and opinion will help you determine how reliable a source is.

How to do it. To recognize a fact, look for information that can be checked elsewhere. Often this type of text tells *who, what, where, when,* or *how much.* If you can find the same information in a reliable source, it's likely a fact.

To recognize opinions, look for such words as *think, feel,* or *believe.* Also look for words that carry a value judgment, such as *most, best, impressive,* or *wonderful.* An author's predictions may be an expression of opinion. For example, "With a little money, we could solve our town's pollution problem." That's the author's opinion.

Try it. As you read this passage, identify facts and opinions. List at least one of each and answer the questions. An example has been done for you.

> *The Chinese Emperor of Qin had the greatest and longest-lasting influence of all the emperors of China. He was born in 259 B.C.E. and became ruler at age 13. Sometimes called the Tiger of Qin, he was very ambitious. He used military might, spies, bribery, and alliances to conquer rival states. Soon he gained power over all of China. He proclaimed himself emperor in 221 B.C.E. During his reign, the emperor created a unified system of laws and writing. He also strengthened the empire against invasion. His tomb covers many square miles. The people of China will always remember him as the man who created a new world.*

Fact	How might you prove this fact?	Opinion	What suggests this is an opinion?
1. The emperor of Qin was born in 259 B.C.E.	Use a history book or encyclopedia	The emperor of Qin had the greatest influence of the Chinese emperors	The word *greatest*
2.			
3.			

Selecting Useful Information

What is it? When you research a topic, you need to determine which information is useful and which isn't. Useful information is relevant, essential, and verifiable. Information is **relevant** if it is connected to your topic. Information is **essential** if you cannot answer your research question without it. Information is **verifiable** if you can find it in other reliable sources.

How to do it. Examine each piece of information in your reading. Does it help define, explain, or give details about your topic? Can you verify the information?

Try it. Suppose you are researching this question: *What was daily life like for a Civil War soldier?* You have found firsthand information in letters from a Union soldier to his mother. In a chart, list information from the reading. Decide if it is relevant, essential, and verifiable for your topic. An example is done for you.

> *For a few days . . . both armies are on very friendly terms. Well today I was out on the line and there was a lot of Rebs there and one of them invited me to go with him . . . Had a great chat . . .*
>
> *Desertions from their army are quite numerous . . . I had on a pair of fine Gaiters and one of them asked me the price. I told him and he said they would cost in Petersburg $150. Common shoes cost 60 & 70 Dolls. Common letter paper 50 cts per sheet & mighty hard to get at that. They say themselves that they have had no coffee or sugar for 4 weeks.*
>
> *You need not be alarmed about my health for I have good heavy blanket and warm clothes. My boots was not very good but we have all drawed a good pair of government shoes . . . There is about half a dozen men in our regiment that are sick.*
>
> —Papers of Tilton C. Reynolds, 1851–1963, Library of Congress: Manuscript Division

Information	Relevant?	Essential?	Verifiable?
Union soldier reports many desertions from the Confederate army	yes, part of a soldier's daily life	maybe not, for this topic	probably

Selecting Credible Sources: Primary Sources

What is it? A **primary source** is a record or an artifact from the past that was created by someone who witnessed an event or lived through an era. Examples are letters, diaries, interviews, photos, and things such as tools, clothing, or weapons.

How to do it. To select a primary source that is **credible,** or believable, you must ask questions about the source.

- Who created this source? What was its purpose?
- Is there any reason to think the creator might exaggerate, leave out important information, or not tell the truth?

You might need to find out more about the source or its creator. You might also compare the source to other views of the same event.

Try it. Suppose you are researching this question: *Who was to blame for the Boston Massacre?* "Boston Massacre" is the American name for a fight between British troops and a crowd of angry colonists in 1770. The colonists started a small riot, and British soldiers killed five of them. Consider the following primary sources, and answer the questions.

1. Trial testimony of Dr. John Jeffries, who treated a wounded colonist who later died
2. Trial testimony of one of the British soldiers who fired at the colonists
3. A flyer entitled "An account of a late military massacre at Boston," published in New York in 1770
4. An engraving that shows soldiers firing on unarmed citizens, created by Paul Revere, a silversmith living in Boston in 1770

Source	Credible or not credible?	Why?	What else would you like to know about the source?
1	not very credible	It is unclear if Jeffries was an eyewitness or not.	Did Jeffries have political leanings toward either the Patriots or the British?
2			
3			
4			

Selecting Credible Sources: Secondary Sources

What is it? A **secondary source** is a record created by someone who did not personally experience the event described. Examples of secondary sources include encyclopedias, almanacs, biographies, and textbooks.

How to do it. To select a secondary source that is **credible,** or believable, you must ask questions about the source.

- Who is the author? What is the author's background? What else has the author written? Does the author belong to a group with a certain point of view?
- How recently was the source created or updated? If it was created long ago, where could you look for more recent sources?
- Why was the source created? Is it meant to give facts or to explain what happened? Does it try to persuade you to see things a certain way?

Try it. Suppose you are researching this question: *What was everyday life like for enslaved Africans in the American colonies?* Consider the following secondary sources, and complete the table. Tell what you would like to know further about each source.

1. *Myths and Realities: Societies of the Colonial South,* by Carl Bridenbaugh, 1952. Bridenbaugh was a professor of American history at the University of California, Berkeley, and at Brown University.
2. *Resource Guide: Slavery,* on Digital History, a U.S. history Web site developed and maintained by the University of Houston, updated December 2005.
3. *American Slavery as It Is: Testimony of a Thousand Witnesses,* published anonymously in 1839. Written by Theodore Dwight Weld, an antislavery activist.
4. *Slavery Defended: The Views of the Old South,* edited by Eric L. McKitrick, 1963. A collection of proslavery writings from the mid-1800s.

Source	Author	Date	Purpose	What else would you like to know about the source?
1	Bridenbaugh	1952	to explain and teach	What else has he written?
2				
3				
4				

Drawing Sound Conclusions

What is it? Sometimes writers state their conclusions directly. Other times it is up to you, the reader, to draw conclusions from the reading. A **sound conclusion** is based on solid evidence and your knowledge of the subject.

How to do it. First, read the passage. What facts are given? Looking at these facts together, what do they suggest to you that is not stated in the reading?

Try it. Read this passage about ancient Greece.

> *In some city-states, aristocrats—wealthy men who had inherited large pieces of land—insisted that the king should be elected instead of inheriting his crown. Then they said the king could rule for only a certain number of years. Eventually, aristocrats in most city-states overthrew the monarchy. By 800 B.C.E., kings no longer ruled most Greek city-states.*

Identify two more facts from the passage. What conclusion could you draw from these facts? How could you test your conclusion to see if it is sound?

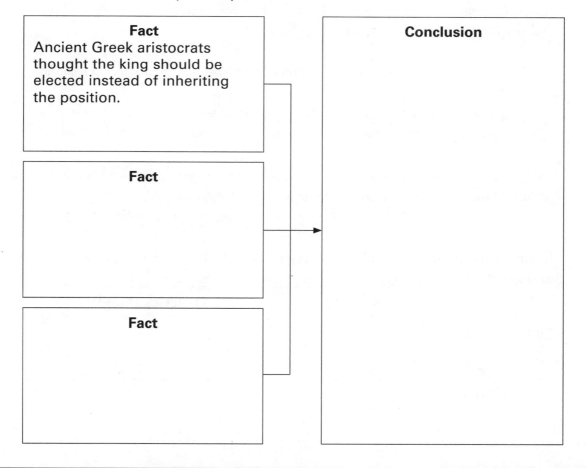

Fact
Ancient Greek aristocrats thought the king should be elected instead of inheriting the position.

Fact

Fact

Conclusion

Identifying Frame of Reference and Point of View

What is it? Someone's frame of reference includes all the things that influence how that person thinks and the way that person sees the world. Point of view is a person's individual opinion or perspective.

How to do it. First, identify everything you know about the writer of the passage. Consider background, age, culture, the historical period in which he or she lived, and beliefs. Next, look for expressions of the person's perspective. They may be stated directly: "I believe that . . ." Or they may be expressed in value judgments, such as "the worst ever . . ." How do you think this person's frame of reference might have influenced his or her point of view?

Try it. During the Civil War, the Union at first refused to enlist African American soldiers. Consider these two quotes from that time.

> *Do you know that this is a white man's government; that the white men are able to defend and protect it; and that to enlist a Negro soldier would be to drive every white man out of the service?*
>
> —Ohio governor David Todd,
> in response to a group of African Americans who asked to form a regiment

> *Why does the government reject the Negro? Is he not a man? Can he not wield a sword, fire a gun, march and countermarch, and obey orders like any other? . . .*
> *Men in earnest don't fight with one hand, when they might fight with two, and a man drowning would not refuse to be saved even by a colored hand.*
>
> —African American antislavery leader Frederick Douglass

Identify the point of view and frame of reference of each man. How do you think frame of reference might have shaped each man's perspective?

	David Todd	**Frederick Douglass**
Point of View		
Frame of Reference		

Identifying Bias, Stereotyping, and Propaganda

What is it? **Bias** is a one-sided or slanted view. A **stereotype** is an oversimplified image of a group or an idea. **Propaganda** means the spreading of one-sided views to influence people's opinions or actions. To evaluate historical evidence, you must be able to recognize bias, stereotyping, and propaganda.

How to do it. To identify bias, look for exaggerations and emotionally charged images or words. Are opinions stated as if they were facts? What information is left out? In what way does the piece focus on one side of an issue?

To recognize a stereotype, look for exaggerations and for overly negative or positive statements or images.

To recognize propaganda, ask yourself: Does the piece present only one side of the story? Does it appeal to people's desire to belong or be part of a group? Does it connect the cause to a respected group or symbol?

Try it. In World War I, the British were at war with the Germans. This poster was created during that war. Answer the questions below.

1. What is the bias of this poster? What emotionally charged words and images does it use?

2. What stereotype of the Germans does this poster present?

3. What stereotype of the British does this poster present?

4. What is the propaganda message of this poster?

Conducting a Cost-Benefit Analysis

What is it? One way to make decisions is to conduct a **cost-benefit analysis** of your options. In this process, you compare the **costs** (disadvantages) of choosing a certain course of action with the **benefits** (advantages) of choosing that course.

How to do it. Identify the option you are considering. Make a list of all the costs of pursuing that option, and another list of the benefits. Compare the two lists. Are there more costs than benefits? Does any one cost weigh too heavily? Are the benefits guaranteed outcomes, or is there a chance they won't happen?

Finally, make the decision. Based on your analysis of the costs and benefits, which choice makes the most sense?

Try it. Suppose you are a young man living in China in 1852. You are trying to decide whether to immigrate to California. You have heard stories of "Gold Mountain"—of great wealth, fine homes, and plenty of food. You have also talked to one man who returned empty-handed. He told you that he was badly treated in California. Meanwhile, your village in China has fallen on hard times. War, poor economic conditions, and overcrowded farms have forced your family into poverty. You have barely enough to eat. You will need to leave your family behind if you go to California.

Conduct a cost-benefit analysis of your option of immigrating to California.

Costs	Benefits
Might be badly treated in California	Could make lots of money in California

Put a star by any costs or benefits that are guaranteed.
Do you consider any of the costs too great?
What choice do you make? Why?

Interpreting Political Cartoons

What is it? Political cartoons appear on the editorial pages of newspapers. They may be funny, but their purpose is to carry a message or opinion. Cartoonists use characters and symbols—animals, people, or objects—to communicate their point. **Interpreting a political cartoon** means figuring out the cartoonist's message.

How to do it. Identify the symbols and characters in the cartoon. What does each one stand for? Are there labels or captions to give you clues? Are the characters and symbols simplified or exaggerated to make a point? What details are emphasized? What action is taking place in the cartoon? Fit these pieces of information together to determine the message of the cartoon.

Try it. Interpret this political cartoon by answering the questions below.

1. What are the characters and symbols in the cartoon, and what does each one represent?

2. How do the words help you identify the cartoonist's intention?

3. What action is taking place in the cartoon?

4. What opinion is the cartoonist expressing?

To the Teacher

Students encounter maps every day inside and outside their classes—in books and on handheld devices, computers, and television screens. Whether they're navigating cities and continents or exploring the world by way of an atlas, students will use map skills throughout their lives.

This Map Skills Toolkit provides support for learning and reviewing the basic skills of reading and interpreting maps of all kinds. It includes handouts for the following:

- oceans and continents
- latitude and longitude
- the global grid
- hemispheres
- compass rose
- map scale
- map titles and symbols

Oceans and Continents

What is it? To locate places on our planet, we need to name its largest features. Water covers nearly three-fourths of Earth's surface. The largest bodies of water are **oceans.** The large land areas that cover the rest of the earth are the **continents.**

How to do it. Find the oceans on the map below. This is really just one big body of water, but geographers usually divide it into four oceans. They are the Atlantic, Pacific, Indian, and Arctic oceans.

Now find the continents. Geographers identify seven continents. From largest to smallest, they are Asia, Africa, North America, South America, Antarctica, Europe, and Australia. Europe and Asia are actually parts of one huge landmass that is sometimes called Eurasia. But geographers usually think of Europe and Asia as two continents because they have different cultures and histories.

Oceans and Continents

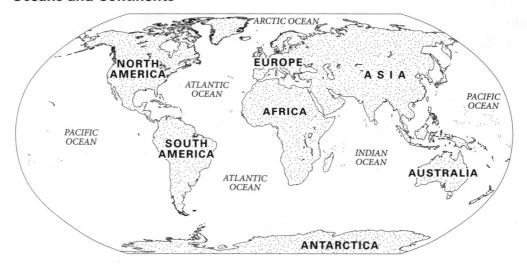

Try it. Use this map to answer the following questions.

1. Which is the most northern ocean on Earth?

2. Which is the most southern continent on Earth?

3. Which continents border the Atlantic Ocean?

4. Which ocean touches three continents? What are they?

5. Which ocean do you think is the largest? Why?

Latitude and Longitude

What is it? Mapmakers draw horizontal and vertical lines around the globe to help us locate places on Earth. The horizontal lines are **parallels of latitude.** The verticals are **meridians of longitude.** Both are measured in degrees.

How to do it. The globe on the left shows how parallels of latitude ring the globe horizontally. Find the equator. It is 0°. Now find the South Pole. It is 90° south latitude, written as 90°S. All of the parallels south of the equator are South latitude. Similarly, the North Pole is 90° north latitude, or 90°N. All parallels north of the equator are North latitude.

The globe on the right shows how meridians of longitude divide the globe in vertical sections between the North and South poles. Find the prime meridian. It is 0° longitude. On the opposite side of the globe is the meridian of 180°. East and west of the prime meridian are 179° of longitude.

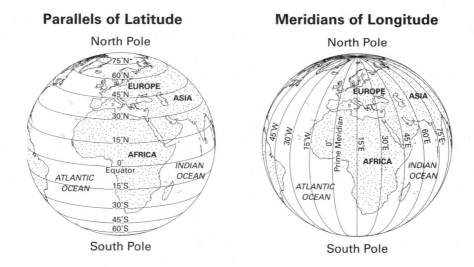

Parallels of Latitude

Meridians of Longitude

Try it. Use these illustrations to help you answer the following questions.
1. Locate the continent of Europe. Which parallels of latitude run through Europe?

2. Locate the prime meridian. Through which continents does it run?

3. Find 30° west longitude. It runs through which ocean?

4. Find the Indian Ocean. Name three meridians of longitude that cross it.

The Global Grid

What is it? The **global grid** shows lines of both latitude and longitude. You can locate the "global address," or *absolute location,* of any place on Earth by finding where its degrees of latitude and longitude cross. For example, the location of Rio De Janeiro, Brazil is 23°S, 44°W. These numbers are called **coordinates**. Latitude always comes first.

How to do it. To find the coordinates of a place, first locate it on a map. Next look up and down to find the degree of latitude. You may have to estimate if the place is between two parallels on a map. Then look left and right to find the degree of longitude. Again, you may need to estimate if the place is between two meridians.

The Global Grid

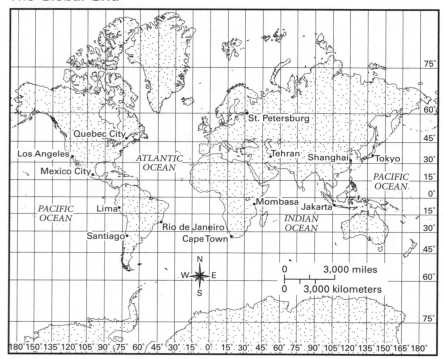

Try it. Use the grid on this map to locate cities around the world.

1. What are the coordinates of St. Petersburg?

2. Which city is located at 47°N, 71°W?

3. What are the coordinates of Shanghai?

4. Estimate the coordinates of Mexico City.

5. Which city is located at 33°N, 118°W?

© Teachers' Curriculum Institute

Hemispheres

What is it? A **hemisphere** is half of a globe or sphere. In geography, a hemisphere is half of planet Earth. Geographers recognize two sets of hemispheres on Earth. One set is the Northern Hemisphere and the Southern Hemisphere. The other set is the Eastern Hemisphere and the Western Hemisphere.

How to do it. Find the equator on the globe below. The equator divides Earth into the Northern and Southern hemispheres. North of the equator lies the Northern Hemisphere. South of the equator lies the Southern Hemisphere.

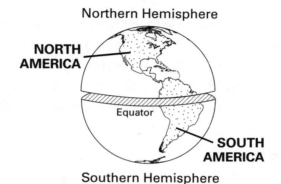

Now find the prime meridian on the second globe. It separates the Eastern and Western hemispheres. To the east of the prime meridian lies the Eastern Hemisphere, while the Western Hemisphere lies to the west of the prime meridian.

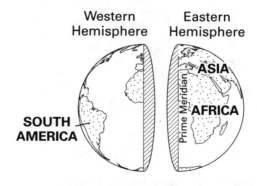

Try it. Answer the following questions, based on the information on these globes.
1. In which hemisphere, Northern or Southern, is the United States?

2. In which hemisphere, Eastern or Western, is Asia?

3. In which two hemispheres is Africa?

4. In which two hemispheres is South America?

Compass Rose

What is it? Mapmakers use a diagram called a **compass rose** to show directions on a map. A simple compass rose has two short lines that cross at right angles. The ends of the lines are labeled N for north, S for south, E for east, and W for west. These are the **cardinal directions**. A more complex compass rose has lines between the cardinal points to show intermediate directions. These lines are labeled NE for northeast, SE for southeast, SW for southwest, and NW for northwest.

How to do it. Use the compass rose to tell where one place is in relation to another. Find Colorado (CO) and Wyoming (WY) on the map below. The compass rose tells you that Colorado is south of Wyoming. This is one way to state its **relative location**. Now find Wisconsin (WI). From the compass rose, you can see that Minnesota (MN) is west of Wisconsin. You can also see that Indiana (IN) is southeast of Wisconsin.

Continental United States

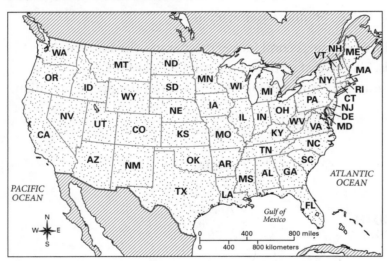

Try it. Use this map to answer the following questions.
1. Which state borders Oregon (OR) on the east? The north?
2. If you traveled from Georgia (GA) to Missouri (MO), in which direction would you go?
3. Find Colorado (CO) and Nebraska (NE). Where is Nebraska in relation to Colorado?
4. Suppose you go north from Texas (TX) to the next state. Then you go to the state to the west. Where would you be?

Map Scale

What is it? Mapmakers include a **scale** to show the relationship between a unit of measure on a map and the actual distance in the real world. The scale tells you how to read the distances on the map. For instance, an inch on a map might equal 10 miles on earth. A map scale usually has two short lines with notches on them. One line measures distance in miles, the other in kilometers.

How to do it. The easiest way to use a map scale is to make a map strip. Find the scale on the map below. Place a strip of paper under the map scale. Mark the scale's notches on the paper, and label the marks with the number of miles or kilometers. Use a ruler to help you extend the notches on your strip. Then place the strip with the "0" mark at one point on the map. Line up the strip with a second point. Now read the closest number on your strip to this second point. You have just figured out the actual distance between two places.

Continental United States

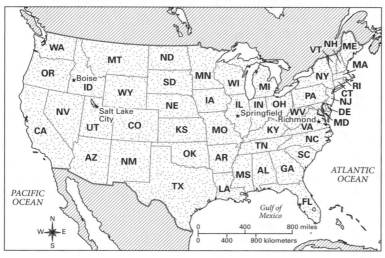

Try it. Practice reading distances using the scale on this map. Then answer the questions below.

1. What does 1 inch equal on this map?
2. About how many miles is it between Springfield, Illinois, and Richmond, Virginia?
3. If you start at Boise, Idaho, and go southeast, how many miles is it to Salt Lake City?
4. Plan a trip of 1,000 miles that goes through at least three states. Where would you start? Where would you end? Which states would you pass through?

Map Titles and Symbols

What is it? The **title** tells you the subject of a map. **Symbols** on a map represent different types of information. Symbols include shapes, colors, and lines. Shapes such as stars can stand for capital cities. Lines can represent borders, highways, and rivers. Areas of colors symbolize regions, such as green for forests. A **legend** lists the symbols on a map in a box and explains what they mean. A map legend is also called a **map key**.

How to do it. Read the map title first. Ask yourself what part of the world the map shows. The title should also tell what type of information the map shows, such as time period, routes, products, population, or climate.

Now look at the map itself. Match up each symbol with its explanation in the legend. Then look at the map as a whole. In your own words, summarize the information that the map presents.

Ancient Greek Trading Routes, About 500 B.C.E.

Try it. Use the map title and legend to answer the following questions.
1. What is the subject of this map? What period of time does it show?
2. What do the heavy solid lines on the map stand for?
3. What do the shaded areas represent?
4. Which product came from both Egypt and Tyras?
5. Which product came only from Persia?

Chapter 2

11: Samuel de Champlain, *Voyages of Samuel de Champlain,* Vol. 2, 1604–1610, trans. Charles Pomeroy Otis, ed. Edmund F. Slafter (Boston: The Prince Society, 1878), at www.books.google.com.

Chapter 5

29: Patrick Henry, "Give Me Liberty or Give Me Death" speech, May 23, 1775, at www.bartleby.com. **30:** Ibid. Thomas Jefferson, in Harry Thayer Mahoney and Marjorie Locke Mahoney, *Gallantry in Action: A Biographic Dictionary of Espionage in the American Revolutionary War* (Lanham, MD: University Press of America, 1999). **31:** Mercy Otis Warren, *Poems, Dramatic and Miscellaneous* (Boston: I. Thomas and E. T. Andrews, 1790), at www.books.google.com. **32:** Felix Holbrook, et al. in "Freedom Petition of Massachusetts Slaves," April 20, 1773, at www.columbia.edu.

Chapter 6

46: Patrick Henry, "Give Me Liberty or Give Me Death" speech, May 23, 1775, at www.bartleby.com. Thomas Jefferson, *Memoirs, Correspondence, and Private Papers of Thomas Jefferson: Late President of the United States,* Vol. 1, ed. Thomas Jefferson Randolph (Charlottesville, VA: F. Carr and Co., 1829), at www.books.google.com.

Chapter 7

52: Thomas Paine, *The American Crisis, No. 1,* at www.bartleby.com. **55:** Ibid.

Chapter 8

74: Major William Pierce, in "Notes of Major William Pierce (Georgia) in the Federal Convention of 1787," at www.avalon.law.yale.edu.

Chapter 11

142: Thomas Jefferson, "First Inaugural Address," March 4, 1801, at www.bartleby.com.

Chapter 13

155: James Fenimore Cooper, *The Last of the Mohicans* (New York: Charles Scribner's Sons, 1919). Davy Crockett, *A Narrative of the Life of David Crockett of the State of Tennessee* (Baltimore: E.L. Carey and A. Hart, 1834), at www.books.google.com. Henry Wadsworth Longfellow, "Paul Revere's Ride," at www.bartleby.com. Washington Irving, *The Legend of Sleepy Hollow,* at www.bartleby.com.

Chapter 18

195: "The Declaration of Sentiments," at www.fordham.edu. **196:** Ibid.

Chapter 20

210: *The American Slave: A Composite Autobiography,* edited by George P. Rawick. Copyright © 1972 by George P. Rawick. Reproduced with permission of ABC-CLIO, LLC. Ibid. **211:** *The American Slave: A Composite Autobiography,* edited by George P. Rawick. Copyright © 1972 by George P. Rawick. Reproduced with permission of ABC-CLIO, LLC. **212:** *The American Slave: A Composite Autobiography,* edited by George P. Rawick. Copyright © 1972 by George P. Rawick. Reproduced with permission of ABC-CLIO, LLC. Charity Bowery, in John W. Blassingame, ed., *Slave Testimony: Two Centuries of Letters, Speeches, Interviews, and Autobiographies* (Baton Rouge, LA: Louisiana State University Press, 1977 [first published 1848, by *The Emancipator*]). **213:** Nat Turner, in Thomas Grey, *Confessions of Nat Turner, The Leader of the Late Insurrection in Southampton, Virginia* (Baltimore, MD: Lucas and Deaver, 1831). *The American Slave: A Composite Autobiography,* edited by George P. Rawick. Copyright © 1972 by George P. Rawick. Reproduced with permission of ABC-CLIO, LLC. **217:** Frederick Douglass, *Life and Times of Frederick Douglass* (Hartford, CT: Park Pub., 1882), at www.books.google.com.

Chapter 21

227: Abraham Lincoln, 1858, at www.bartleby.com.

Chapter 22

229: John Gibbon, in Jeffry D. Wert, *Gettysburg: Day Three* (New York: Touchstone, 2001). **230:** Lewis Armistead, in Jeffry D. Wert, *Gettysburg: Day Three* (New York: Touchstone, 2001).

Chapter 27

269: Andrew Carnegie, *The Gospel of Wealth and Other Timely Essays* (BiblioBazaar, 2009). John D. Rockefeller, in Allen Freeman Davis and Harold D. Woodman, *Conflict and Consensus in Modern American History,* Vol. 2, 4th ed. (Lexington, MA: D. C. Heath, 1976). John D. Rockefeller, in John T. Flynn, *God's Gold: The Story of Rockefeller and His Times* (John T. Flynn, 1932). **270:** Progressive Party, at www.waprogparty.org. Robert La Follette, in F. E. Haynes, "La Follette and La Follettism," *The Atlantic* (October 1924), at www.theatlantic.com. **271:** Mary Harris Jones, *Autobiography of Mother Jones* (Mineola, NY: Dover Pub., 2004 [first published 1925 by Charles H. Kerr and Co.]). John Muir, in James Mitchell Clarke, *The Life and Adventures of John Muir* (San Diego, CA: Word Shop, 1980). **272:** W. E. B. Du Bois, in Ronald H. Bayor, *The Columbia Documentary History of Race and Ethnicity in America* (New York: Columbia University Press, 2004). Upton Sinclair, *The Way Out: What Lies Ahead for America* (Los Angeles, CA: Upton Sinclair, 1933). **273:** Emmeline Pankhurst, at www.quotationsbook.com. **284:** Andrew Carnegie, in Joseph Frazier Wall, *Andrew Carnegie* (New York: Oxford University Press, 1970). **286:** Upton Sinclair, *The Jungle,* introduction by Jane Jacobs (New York: Random House, 2006 [first published 1906 by Upton Sinclair]).

Chapter 29

297: "Transcript of Civil Rights Act (1964)," at www.ourdocuments.gov.

Photographs

Chapter 2
11: Library of Congress

Chapter 4
22: Marston, James Brown (1775-1817). "Old State House". Oil on canvas, 1801. MHS image number 71. Courtesy of the Massachusetts Historical Society.

Unit 1 Timeline Challenge Cards
24 BR: Library of Congress **24 BL:** Library of Congress **24 TR:** RF/Wikimedia **25 TL:** RF/Picture Research Consultants & Archives **25 TR:** RF/Picture Research Consultants & Archives **25 BL:** RF/Private Collection/Picture Research Consultants & Archives **25 BR:** Library of Congress **26 TL:** Library of Congress **26 TR:** RF/Wikimedia **26 BL:** Library of Congress **26 BR:** RF/Wikimedia

Chapter 5
38 L: Library of Congress **38 R:** Library of Congress

Unit 2 Timeline Challenge Cards
59 TR: Library of Congress **59 BL:** Library of Congress **59 BR:** RF/Picture Research Consultants & Archives **59 TL:** Library of Congress **60 TL:** Library of Congress **60 BR:** Library of Congress **60 BL:** Library of Congress **60 TR:** Courtesy of Lou Sideris/Minute Man National Historical Park. **61 TL:** Library of Congress **61 TR:** Library of Congress **61 BR:** Library of Congress **61 BL:** Library of Congress

Unit 3 Timeline Challenge Cards
133 TR: RF/Picture Research Consultants & Archives **133 TL:** National Archives **133 BR:** RF/JVT/istockphoto.com **134 TR:** Library of Congress **134 TL:** Library of Congress **134 BR:** RF/Eliza Snow/istockphoto.com **134 BL:** RF/webking/istockphoto.com

Chapter 14
164: The New-York Historical Society.

Unit 4 Timeline Challenge Cards
166 TR: Library of Congress **166 TR:** Library of Congress **166 BR:** Allyn Cox/Architect of the Capitol **166 BL:** The Granger Collection, New York **167 TL:** Library of Congress **167 TR:** Library of Congress **167 BL:** RF/Hulton Archive/istockphoto.com **167 BR:** Library of Congress **168 TL:** Library of Congress **168 BL:** Library of Congress **168 BR:** RF/Picture Research Consultants & Archives **168 TR:** Library of Congress

Unit 5 Timeline Challenge Cards
192 TR: Library of Congress **192 BL:** RF/Picture Research Consultants & Archives **192 TR:** Library of Congress **192 BR:** Library of Congress **193 TL:** Approaching Chimney Rock by William Henry Jackson: Scotts Bluff National Monument. **193 BL:** Library of Congress **193 BR:** Franklin D. Roosevelt Library **193 TR:** RF/Brandon Seidel/123RF **194 TL:** California State Library **194 BL:** Library of Congress **194 BR:** Library of Congress

Unit 6 Timeline Challenge Cards
219 TR: RF/Norman Reid/istockphoto.com **219 BL:** RF/Picture Research Consultants & Archives **219 BR:** RF/Picture Research Consultants & Archives **219 TL:** RF/Boston Directory 1868/Wikimedia **220 BR:** RF/Picture Research Consultants & Archives **220 BL:** Library of Congress **220 TL:** Library of Congress **220 TR:** Library of Congress **221 TR:** Library of Congress **221 BR:** Library of Congress **221 BL:** Library of Congress **221 TL:** National Archives

Chapter 23
242 TR: Library of Congress **242 BR:** Library of Congress **242 BL:** RF/Wikimedia **243 BR:** Library of Congress **243 TR:** Library of Congress **243 TL:** Library of Congress **243 BL:** Library of Congress **244 BR:** Library of Congress **244 BL:** Library of Congress **244 TL:** Appomattox Court House National Historic Park **244 TR:** Library of Congress

Chapter 25
258: Library of Congress

Unit 8 Timeline Challenge Cards
266 TL: RF/Picture Research Consultants & Archives **266 TR:** Library of Congress **266 BL:** RF/Jason Yoder/123RF **266 BR:** Library of Congress **267 TR:** U.S. Department of the Interior National Park Service Edison National Historic Site **267 TL:** Library of Congress **267 BL:** Library of Congress **267 BL:** Library of Congress **268 TR:** Library of Congress **268 TL:** Library of Congress **268 BL:** Library of Congress **268 BL:** Library of Congress

Chapter 28
291: Library of Congress

Unit 9 Timeline Challenge Cards
299 TR: Library of Congress **299 BL:** Library of Congress **299 TL:** Library of Congress **299 BR:** Library of Congress **300 TL:** National Archives **300 TR:** Library of Congress **300 BL:** RF/Picture Research Consultants & Archives **300 BR:** Library of Congress **301 BL:** National Archives **301 TL:** Library of Congress **301 TR:** RF/Wikimedia **301 TR:** Library of Congress

Art

Chapter 7
54: Len Ebert

Chapter 8
80–109: Rosiland Solomon
117: QYA Design Studio

Chapter 9
127: QYA Design Studio

Chapter 11
137–138: Rosiland Solomon
139: Gary Undercuffler

Chapter 12
147: Gary Undercuffler

Chapter 27
272–280: Rosiland Solomon